MEET ME IN BEIRUT

MEET ME IN BEIRUT

BASED ON A TRUE STORY

ROBERT TIBOLT

BATTLE BORN ARTS, LLC

Meet Me in Beirut is a work of fact-based fiction. The events and conversations from this book are a reflection of the author's experiences, recollections, and inferences. Some names have been altered to honor the privacy of those involved.

Edited by Shelley Chung and Jared Kuritz
Proofread by Cindy Doty
Cover and Interior Design by Gwyn Flowers / gkscreative.com

Publishing Inquiries:
Battle Born Arts
11700 W. Charleston Blvd. #170-680
Las Vegas, NV 89135

Media Inquiries:
STRATEGIES PR
P.O. Box 178122
San Diego, CA 92177

ISBN: 978-1-948792-14-1 (trade paperback)
ISBN: 978-1-948792-15-8 (ePub)
ISBN: 978-1-948792-17-2 (mobi)

FIRST EDITION

First Printed in the United States.

First Published in the United States by Battle Born Arts, LLC

NOTE TO THE READER

The following is based on a true story. All of the events are written
to the best of my recollection. Some inferences were necessary
to address questions that had no answers.

"MEET ME in BEIRUT"

Bill and Bob 1975

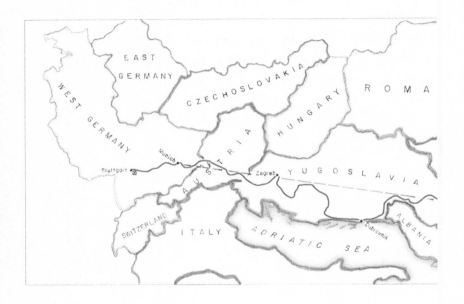

Map of parts of Europe and the Middle East showing
driving path to, and air path back, from Stuttgart to Beirut.

LEGEND   Auto Path ─────   Auto Wreck ⊗

           Air Path ── ──   Mountain +

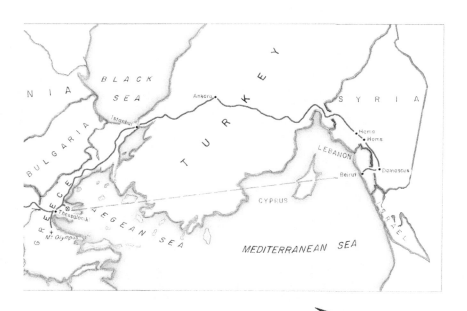

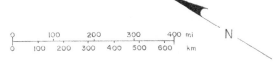

| 0 | 100 | 200 | 300 | 400 mi |
| 0 | 100 | 200 | 300 | 400 | 500 | 600 | km |

N

CHAPTER 1

I sat in German class, Literature of the Twentieth Century, daydreaming as Fräulein Basner spoke in German about *Biedermann und die Brandstifter*. At least I was daydreaming about Germany. I followed her pretty well. I had studied German for eight years, read all the inane monographs, listened to all the stilted conversations on records (*"Guten Tag, Luisa. Wie geht's?"*), conversed in class better than most; but I still didn't know much about Germany. Everyone knew the high points: a regimented, superior people who dished it out and also received it beyond what the world had seen in centuries; a technical beehive of unparalleled origins of the modern world; a land of beer drinking and hearty living. What about the rest? What are the people really like? Are they friendly? Not by reputation, but perhaps in their own way they are. How about the girls? Lots of pretty blondes no doubt, but are they kind? Are they fun? What do they think of Americans? Have they gotten over it, or do they still harbor deep resentments that can never go away? These thoughts drifted into more mundane and reachable thoughts: How's the food? I know the beer is great, and I'm pretty sure the wine is too. How will my German family be?

Will they be easy and accommodating, or rigid and a pain in the ass to live with? Will they like me?

"Bob, *was denken Sie über Feuer wie ein Thema?*"

What do I think about fire as a theme in a book about an arsonist? This is the sort of question that generally got me on the wrong side of some of my professors. It is challenging when what you want to say is anathema to what they want you to say. I said something about matches being repressed anger and the lighting of the fire its uncontrollable release. She liked it well enough and moved on as I moved on to more thoughts of Germany: meeting my friends who would be there, having a free term to travel before my foreign study program was to begin—a dream of a dream.

Christmas vacation came and went as it had been doing while I was away at college. I returned home and saw my family, spent time with my friends, and thought more about Germany. I traveled back to Hanover (New Hampshire, that is), then would take the train to Montreal and fly Lufthansa to Stuttgart via Frankfurt. My hometown buddy Bill, just finishing an academic quarter abroad in Germany, and his brother Joe would meet me at the airport. It was the perfect scenario: best buddies with a car in Europe, three months to travel and have fun, and no limits. Joe was visiting Bill over the holiday and would be returning to the States a couple of days after I arrived. It was a great setup. I had not been able to make it real in my mind, though; I kept thinking and thinking of what it would be and still I couldn't solidify my vacuous thoughts and feelings. We did have a tentative plan to drive to Istanbul, travel down the Aegean coast of Turkey, take a ferry to Athens, and then return to Stuttgart, actually Beutelsbach, in three months.

I was in my fraternity room trying to organize my duffel bag, looking for a Dopp kit, trying to make sure I had all my tickets and papers, all the usual travel details that the entropy of the world tries to scatter and hide. I took a break and headed down to the basement. It was December 30, not a big Monday night at a college. Most of the guys weren't back yet, but there were enough to have a few beers and play beer pong, Wales tails, and other assorted contests of the basement pentathlon. I was taking the red-eye out the following night and the train tonight. As eleven approached, I gathered my things and knocked on Froggie's door. He was undoubtedly with his girlfriend the Toad. He had said he could give me a ride to the White River Junction station. He was as good as his word, in spite of having to extricate himself mid-stroke. He dropped me off and there I stood, snow falling, train waiting, fellow travelers milling; my adventure about to begin. It would be my first time riding a train other than the little tourist rides I had taken as a kid. I was ready and eager, still lost in a dream of time and space separating me from my destination, at least the first one.

The charm of train travel recedes quickly after departure. The seat was comfortable enough, it was not crowded; there was a faint odor of a public restroom mixed with some kind of railroad smell. Tolerable certainly. My fellow travelers were few and quiet, demonstrating only a desire to sleep. They looked like emmets and newts, New Hampshiremen and Vermonters. Maybe I looked like one of them too. I slept and woke up as we were crossing into Canada with surprisingly little fanfare. Some uniformed guys came through and asked for ID; I was pleased to show my passport, stampless though it was. I would certainly fix that shortly. On we traveled through my first foreign country of the trip: bare trees, conifers, snow, and little else.

We arrived early in the morning just as the eastern sky began to brighten. It was cold: Montreal-in-the-middle-of-winter cold; nostril-sticking, snow-crunching, ear-burning cold. I had the entire day to enjoy Montreal. My grandmother was French Canadian and had grown up here in her early life, so I was happy to spend time in her town. She had told me about the Queen Elizabeth hotel, and I headed there on foot; it was right across the street. It felt so good to walk in. The warmth and luxury, the forest green carpet and roaring fire, and the small, French-looking people all gave me a feeling of differentness and comfort. I found the luggage valet and checked my bag. I tramped across the carpet and generated a spark as my hand touched the railing at the stairwell going down. I remembered something my grandmother and her friend Mrs. Darcy had told me, about a restaurant in the hotel that I must see, the Beaver Club. I took the stairs and found myself standing in front of it. I saw movements in the bar through the stained-glass windows on each side of the door. I could hear robust singing and laughing. I rapped on the door, then banged on it. After a moment, a man came to the door.

"*Oui?*"

"I am interested in seeing the Beaver Club."

"I am afraid that we are not open to the general public at the moment, sir. This is a private party whose event has run over. Please come back at three o'clock, sir, and we will welcome you in then."

"Would you consider just letting me come in to look around? I won't bother anyone. My grandmother is from Montreal and told me to visit the Beaver Club. I'm flying to Europe this evening and may not be able to come back at three."

He hesitated, then shook his head almost imperceptibly as he opened the door and motioned me in with two impatient waves. We walked to the bar.

"Please just look around and don't regard the patrons. You will return the favor that I do for you by please doing this. Would you like something to drink?"

"I'll have whatever the men are drinking."

He filled a glass mug from a tap with a dark, foamy beer and handed it to me.

"Thank you, sir. How much do I owe you?"

"It is taken care of."

"Thank you, sir, and thank you to your guests."

I hoisted the mug and sampled the brew. It was good. The room was elegant with brick walls on two sides and cream-colored wallpaper on the other two, these sides hung with framed pieces of ancient significance. The carpet had a quadrangular pattern that was handsome, short piled, and rich. I was pleased to spend some time here and would be happy to report back to my grandmother.

They resumed singing but now it was with a whispered voice along with gesticulations with their hands and mugs. I watched them through the reflections from the paintings on the wall. I tried to appear disinterested. I finished my beer and waved to the hotelier before walking out. I lingered outside the door for a few moments listening to the song or chant that they were singing, then walked back to the lobby.

I spent the rest of the day browsing around downtown Montreal. I enjoyed the French atmosphere. I had several small meals interspersed between leisurely strolls down the avenues. Dusk approached and I made my way back to the Queen Elizabeth to retrieve my bag, then walked to the Gare Centrale to find the airport limousine. Upon arriving at the airport, I checked my bag with Lufthansa and found a shower facility. Freshened now, I made my way to the gate. Several other passengers had arrived even before me. I began to hear words and larger bits of conversation in German. It became apparent now that German was a language and not just an academic exercise. It came to life before me in a startling, visceral way that I would never forget. My image of Germany and my adventure began to take shape.

CHAPTER 2

The hours passed quickly as I sat immersed in German, gaining more in understanding than in all my prior hours of forced conversation and study, or so it seemed. We boarded the 707, and I ended up sitting next to a nice, rotund, middle-aged German lady. We began to speak German. It was even more thrilling than listening to it. I could speak it, and she could understand me. She also spoke better English than my German, so she helped me out when I was at a loss. She also had a private collection of airline-sized bottles of booze. We talked and drank until we each passed out or fell asleep.

When I awoke, I could see pale light starting to come through the windows. Soon it was clearly light outside, and it was announced that we would shortly be landing in Frankfurt. I told my seatmate that I was going on to Stuttgart. She told me that the dialect there was especially hard to understand, even for a German. We landed and I said *auf wiedersehen* to my friend. I followed the crowd to a bus, and we rode to a terminal. I was shunted by way of glass walkways to the domestic flight area. I was surprised that I didn't proceed through customs, and shocked by the abundance of soldiers with machine guns. Through the windows I could see more soldiers outside, some in fortified areas, some around half-tracks, all with machine pistols. The Baader-Meinhof and Red Brigade came to mind as I hoped they didn't suspect me of anything nefarious.

I waited forty-five minutes and boarded the flight to Stuttgart. It was a smaller jet. They served a nice breakfast of coffee, rolls, butter, cheese, and jelly. Bill and Joe were fun guys, and I knew that we would have a great time. I was arriving on January 2, 1975. *What a great way to start a new year*, I thought.

We landed and deplaned using a traditional stairway wheeled up to the plane. I made my way to a waiting area. My bag appeared, I retrieved it, and went through some doors to *Grenzkontrolle*. Just then I saw Joe. He waved me over.

"What about customs?"

"Fuck customs."

I ducked under a rope and walked outside with Joe. It seemed strange but I did as I was told and there was Bill, parked at the curb in a dirty, off-white VW square back.

"Where the fuck have you been, T? We expected you yesterday. We were here for hours waiting for you. Joe is going back tomorrow, the little dick, and you fucked us."

"Sorry, "Willard." I thought I said I was arriving on the second." He always called me by my nickname, "T", and I called him by his, which was Willard.

Joe gave me a "see-what-I-mean?" look and we were off to the *Gasthaus*.

I was jet-lagged but feeling good. I watched the scenery as Bill raced the little car. There were big convex mirrors on street corners, and the stoplights went from red to yellow to green. We crested a hill, and I looked down into a quaint valley with three small villages all tucked in. The roads were small and clean with tidy berms and sidewalks everywhere. We landed at our destination, *die Rosen.*

In impressively-uttered German, Bill ordered three beers. It was now late morning. We were not the only people drinking; everyone else was pounding beers. I looked around and saw little games on the walls that people were playing. Food was being served and marvelous-looking stuff it was. Soon a couple of sleazy-looking guys walked in. They were Bill's local friends, Guy and Steiner. They ordered up. The waitress kept track of our tab by making marks on the *Bierdeckel.* Rapidly, there were a lot of marks on it. At the crowd's request, the waitress brought over a glass boot, *der Stiefel.* It was filled with beer and the game began. The object was to finish the contents of the boot so that the person before you who had handed it off to you had to buy the next one. The strategy of course was not to leave a chugable amount. Each drink was preceded by a ritualistic three-way gesture of elbow on the table, forearm to the table, and two fingers rapping the *Stiefel.* I caught on after buying the first two rounds.

One can imagine where this was going. American and German friends of Bill came and went. Food came and it tasted even better than it looked, so fresh and perfect. We settled up and drove to a *Weinstube* for a change of pace. We drank white wine that was scrumptious, not that I would know the difference. We ate wurst of different varieties. I began to understand why Bill was so fat.

The evening progressed with some illicit behavior of the hash kind and a decision to drive up to the *Ratskeller* on top of a hill. Bill was driving hard up the windy mountain road when he lost control and we slid off onto the hillside and into an apple tree. We were all belted in; no one was hurt. The right front quarter panel was crushed into the tree. Bill

MEET ME IN BEIRUT

was groaning, "Oh no." Joe said very calmly, "Now you did it, Willard."
I guess things had really begun.

"Have you been drinking, Bill?" asked the director of the Stanford
program in German. Joe's eyes rolled back when Bill answered, *"Nein."*
Herr Professor Eggers looked at Bill and said, "I understand." The whole
thing was thankfully a blur that lasted until morning. Bill's car had been
towed to a shop that Steiner worked in. The police were appropriately
managed, and the farmer was compensated for the loss of his tree by
the Stanford slush fund. Everybody was happy.

It was arranged that Guy would drive Joe to the airport. We all went
and said our good-byes to Joe. Not the best way to end a visit, but we
were still able to laugh and wish each other well.

"Try not to kill yourself," was the last thing Joe said.

Bill and I spent the next few days on foot in Beutelsbach. We were
staying with Frau Zeyer at her *Fremdenzimmer* in an immaculate room.
Everyone heard about the crash so there was a lot to talk about, to Bill's
chagrin. We were now forced to wait for his car to be fixed before we
could leave. Each day, we stopped by and visited with Steiner as he gave
us updates. There were some other problems besides the quarter panel,
so we had to wait for parts. As would be expected, the Germans were
very thorough and would not release the car until it was perfect. Bill did
decline waiting for a paint job, so the involved area showed the Bondo,
a pinky red-brown that didn't go well with the off-white of the rest of
the car. We had to put up with the shit that Steiner's colleagues were
giving Bill in *Schwäbisch*, the local dialect. As predicted, it was unintelligible except for a few words. It was all in good fun, though. The same
thing would have happened in any small town in America.

We did some fun things while we waited. Guy's uncle was a black-
smith in the next town over. We drove there with Guy. His uncle—a
burly, seemingly humorless Schwab—forced *Kirschwasser* from his still

on us. That went well. Then on Sunday morning we enjoyed the tradition of *Frühschoppen*, in which the men all go to the bar and get shit-faced while the women make breakfast.

Finally, the work was done, and the car was ready. We had prepared our travel kit that included sleeping bags, money, passports, and a portable cassette player. We said our *Tschüss's* to our friends in Beutelsbach, got on the autobahn, and made our way to *München* and the *Hofbräuhaus*.

CHAPTER 3

Das *Hofbräuhaus* is a remarkable cavern of beer drinking and merriment. The proverbial oompah band played on. Large young women stronger than I carried one-liter steins of beer ten to a hand and distributed them precisely and efficiently. We developed an attraction for the steins and removed them surreptitiously to the trunk of Bill's car. We had collected a dozen or so before we were caught red-handed by the security fellows. We had to carry them all back in. We kept drinking and eating and carrying more out to the trunk, though, so we were able to reestablish our collection.

On we traveled by autobahn through Bayern until we entered Austria. The scenery was beautiful, the food and *Gemütlichkeit* were fabulous, and the skiing looked impressive. The road carried us to Yugoslavia, the first really different place on our trip.

We crossed the border after paying ten marks for a visa. We were then almost immediately stopped by a cop, our first experience in an unintelligible language. This time it cost fifty deutsche marks (DM);

in exchange, the officer gave Bill a stack of cheaply-printed squares of paper, each with a "10" on it. After the cop turned around, Bill threw them out the window in disgust.

"This country blows," was all he said.

Yugoslavia was no Austria. The woods were dark and eerie. It was the middle of winter in a steady rain—dead of night in total darkness—and we would see groups of people standing for no apparent reason by the side of the road. It was creepy. There were clouds of unknown vapors that smelled like a cross between raw sewage and crude oil. We were forced to stop and sleep in the car. Bill didn't think much of my driving skills; he had some evidence for thinking that. We awoke a few hours later, both shivering and with our teeth literally chattering.

"Get up and get us out of here," Bill moaned.

I knew he was desperate if he wanted me to drive. The cold was horrible, but there was no frost. How is that possible? There was something evil and insidious about it, about Yugoslavia. I drove until the heater started working, then Bill took over.

We entered Zagreb. Everything was grey and ugly, with brown water stains below each window. The high-rise apartments were lined up by the dozens. With the cold and our memories of the evil forest, we decided to drive on and get out of this place as fast as we could. Bill had a lead foot ordinarily, but he really was positively demented now. We did stop at a store to buy some food. The shelves were almost empty; all the items in the store could have been displayed on a single shelf. We managed to find three cans of sardines, two loaves of bread, and a bottle of wine, so we were good. We kept driving relentlessly after buying some gas with DM. After a few more hours we stopped at what looked like a run-down house that had a few cars parked in front. It smelled good and we were seated by the host, who spoke German. He made a point of taking good care of us and brought smoky, spicy lamb; yogurt sauces; flatbread with flakes of carbon right out of the wood oven; wine and cheese. It was so good. The locals were quite animated, conversations coming in waves, rising to a crescendo of anger. I was glad they weren't mad at us. We thanked our host with genuine enthusiasm, paid him handsomely in DM, and kept on course.

We continued driving through rugged little mountains and primitive dwellings, herds of sheep and goats and children. We then crested what was apparently a coastal range and brought the Adriatic Sea into view. This first glimpse of the Mediterranean was spectacular. The water was glacier blue and calm. Rocky spines of grey mountains and hills left their green tunics and fell to a narrow coastal strip crowded with civilization. Several islands of varying sizes lay in the waning light. We saw a convoy of ships steaming south in the passage between the mainland and the islands. There was a single large naval vessel, like a cruiser, surrounded fore and aft by different kinds of support craft including a destroyer and patrol boats. Overhead was a helicopter buzzing nervously about. The significance of the group was lost on us, but it looked impressive and efficient and very determined.

Our road wound slowly down by switchback after switchback, but not before following the coast from above for several miles. This rough little road hugged a cliffside and tempted drivers with a sheer drop to the water. Amenities like guardrails were absent. Willard always enjoyed hard driving, but even he got wide-eyed and muttered, "Oooooooh, shit!" several times. We were southbound and on the water side of the road. The view was more than spectacular; it became plain scary. I could spit out my window and hit water from five hundred feet. We didn't say much as we crept down. Willard got his confidence back after a bit, and he began to attack the downgrade, but gently. We finally reached sea level. We were at the edge of a town, and from the map it looked like we were about twenty kilometers from Dubrovnik. Then we noticed a roadblock.

"Papieren, bitte."

We had been flagged down to the side of the road. There were soldiers everywhere, scattered all down the road through town. We looked at each other with a here-we-go-again look. The soldiers left with our passports, and we sat in the car for half an hour. We watched the convoy glide south down the inlet; it seemed to slow and hold its position not too far down, maybe near Dubrovnik. We frankly didn't mind sitting in the quiet after a hard day of driving. One of the guys came back with our passport, nodded authoritatively, grimaced, and growled, "Go." We complied. We were stopped twice more on the road, five more times in the little town, and then had another long wait at the edge of Dubrovnik. It was dark, but we could see soldiers and military vehicles hanging around everywhere. We were starting to get used to it.

To conserve cash, and in order to utilize Bill's superior financial position, we looked for a place that took Master Charge (MC). We found a strip of decent-looking hotels right on the water and parked the car. The first one was too expensive, the second was a dive, but the third one was nice, overlooked the water, and it seemed like the guy gave us a sweet deal. We grabbed our filthy belongings from the car and rode the small creaky elevator to our room. It was dinky but not too bad. The back door opened up to a veranda overlooking the water. The convoy was parked right out our window. The moon was rising over an island, the air was cool with a soft breeze; it was romantic. Then I saw Willard standing there, naked, his belly hanging out, aiming for the shower. So much for romance.

CHAPTER 4

He showered while I unpacked my few remaining clean clothes. I hoped we would be able to wash our clothes and feel like human beings for a few days. He stepped out of the bathroom with one towel around his waist, and was rubbing under it with his hand, looking at me and making the face that you make while you scratch, teeth clenched.

"You fucker—stay away from me."

The shower was wonderful; there wasn't much velocity, but the water stayed hot. I washed my hair twice and used both soap and shampoo. I felt great. I climbed out of the shower, dried off, and then Willard stuck his head in.

"Let's go eat. I'm shtaaaarving."

We dressed in our cleanest clothes and rode down to the lobby. We were both bushed and decided to eat in the hotel restaurant. It was separate from the hotel, in a small building at the water's edge; it was surrounded by large boulders, almost in a grotto, and was covered by ivy. There were a few stained-glass windows on the landward side, but no windows on the water side. We walked into a dark, quiet room. In one corner sat an older couple, wordless and angry looking. On the other side sat a younger man with a woman. He had a large mustache and was dressed nicely with a tie. She was not attractive. We asked to be seated near the younger couple.

We ordered beer and wine. Neither was spectacular, but both tasted great. We asked the waiter what the specialty was; he mentioned something unintelligible and repeated the exact same name when we asked, "Huh?"

"It is a local fish—very good."

Our young neighbor with the mustache had come to our rescue.

"We'll both have that."

We began to talk with him; she didn't speak English or German.

"She is stupid—from Albania."

"From the map it looks like the shortest way to Thessaloniki is through Albania. Maybe she can tell us some places to go. There isn't very much on the map."

Our friend began to smile at the first sentence, laughed aloud with the second, and was absolutely out of control with the last.

"There is not a thing on the map, because there is not a thing in Albania. The streets are not paved, there are no stores, there are no cars, there are no businesses, there is nothing. You cannot enter Albania, and you cannot leave. You do not want to, and cannot, visit Albania, my friends. I will buy you a beer—you are very entertaining."

He laughed intermittently all night long, and I think he did it every time that he thought about our driving through Albania. He was right about one thing: the fish was good. It was a bony, broiled fish in its skin with white flesh. I swallowed about five bones.

"Don't worry, they won't even make it into the commode."

He was quite a card. He told us about Yugoslavia. He said it wasn't really a country, but that Tito had held things together with an iron fist.

"He is here tonight, in Dubrovnik. Would you like to meet him?"

"Sure, but we don't really have any nice clothes."

He laughed heartily again.

"I am sorry. I am rude. He is old and surrounded by soldiers. I do not think even his mother can see him. There is a conference here about the water pollution in the Mediterranean. Tito brought his navy with him. I must watch what I say."

He looked around and gulped the last swig of wine.

"I must take this sow to bed."

I almost gagged on my wine with that, and we all howled for a few moments with laughter. We said good-bye to our friends. I grasped the lady's hand in mine, kissed it, and said, "Good night, my sow." Willard smiled and said to her, "You're hideously ugly." She glowed and loved the attention. Our friend thanked us for being so gracious. Willard and I finished everything on our table, charged the meal to our room, and walked back. We were asleep in minutes.

The next morning we woke up late, around noon. It was sunny. The air had some warmth to it. We decided to go swimming. We walked down to the lobby with our towels and found the beach that we could see below our balcony. The sun was strong enough to feel on our skin, but the beach was empty.

"Oh, well, no babes."

We went for a very brief dip. The water was actually cold. It was a very strange blue, a blue I had never seen before in any ocean, nor in any lake, pond, or stream. I was suspicious. I figured the reason that they were having the conference with Tito was because there was some problem. I was anxious to shower when we got back to the room.

We found a washer and dryer in the basement and took care of the laundry problem. Then we went for a walk. We soon approached an area surrounded by a thick plaster wall, colored between salmon and tan. We followed it to a portal and walked into the old city of Dubrovnik. It was beautiful. The buildings were stucco with red or variegated tile roofs, wedged among each other between narrow, windy, cobbled streets. It was on a point that jutted into the water, with an island off its prow to port. There were mostly homes, but we found a restaurant that had the MC logo, and we stopped for a fine meal. We strolled through the Old City all afternoon. The walls seemed to take on the color of the sun and glowed with an orange luminescence as dusk approached. We walked back to the hotel. We unknowingly began a tradition that would periodically comprise our evening's entertainment.

"Let's buy a bottle of booze."

"I bet the shit is expensive, Willard."

"We'll see if we can get it with MC."

"Right."

We did it. We found a store near the hotel with bottles for sale. There was one small detail. Willard drank scotch, and I drank bourbon. And neither one liked the other. We drank scotch that night, with the agreement that the next bottle would be bourbon.

At the room we played gin rummy and drank scotch. I got plastered. I hated the taste of scotch, and it really got me fucked up. I was literally bouncing off walls in the hallway to the bathroom. Willard was beside himself.

"You Dartmouth fuckers are such badasses. You little fucking girl."

"Eat shit and die, Willard. I'll see you in Lynchburg, Tennessee, up to your gills in Jack Daniel's."

I think I said something like that, and then I immediately passed out.

That was basically Yugoslavia. We stayed a few more days in Dubrovnik and then began another mad dash to the next possible site of civilization: Thessaloniki, Greece. We wound our way back into the mountains for one last fling at Yugoslav-Transylvania. We were less disturbed this time. We followed the road into Macedonia in southern Yugoslavia. It began to look more like normal mountain and forest. The Greek border was a breeze; I really have very little to report on this leg of the trip. More lamb, wine, bad beer, friendly people, and foul weather—more of the same—accompanied us. Thessaloniki was nothing special to the uninitiated eye: another drab city in the rain. It is a port, located at the end of a blind gulf at the north end of the Aegean. It was second city of the Byzantine Empire. My clearest memory of entering the city occurred when we went into the lobby of a B Hotel looking for the Master Charge sign, and seeing Kojak banging away in Greek on a small black-and-white TV. The crowd didn't even notice us. They accepted our plastic, and we were once again happy to have our stopping place be decent and essentially free.

The initial part of our stay was uneventful. We were introduced to gyros for the first time, and they became our staple. We tried to branch out on one occasion that was especially memorable. The first night we were out walking, and it was raining and bitter cold. We happened to walk by a restaurant that had an immense stainless-steel vat on display through the window, seemingly full of chicken soup. It was steaming and the man was stirring it with a wooden spoon about the size of a canoe paddle. We were hungry and cold. We thought we were the luckiest guys in the world. We went in, sat down, and ordered two large bowls of the stuff. The bread came first and it was good. The soup came and we both dug in with gusto. We almost gagged simultaneously as we smelled and tasted the soup. It was evidently not chicken, and it was nasty. We learned later that it was tripe.

"Back to gyros!"

The next day we looked at the map. From the underbelly of Macedonia hung down a peninsula with three slender spits of land at its end. Khalkidhiki is the peninsula. The northernmost of the fingers is Athos. We learned that it was the location of some twenty-six Greek Orthodox monasteries, most of them carved into rocky mountainsides, and that no women were allowed. We decided to drive out there on that day, and, in the interests of sexual equality, visit the island of Lesbos at a later time. We gassed up the car and headed south. The terrain was a low coastal plain with some small hills. It was mostly pasture with few trees. The rain had cleared out. The sun was shining. We felt the first real Mediterranean warmth. Willard was taking it easy at the wheel, and we had the windows down with our arms out. This idyllic scene continued for a few moments. We were going slowly around a sharp corner on dry roadway. It was on an embankment of about five feet above a field. Imperceptibly, we began to slide off our track, as though we were on an oil slick. Willard caught it and began to steer into the slide, but we were totally out of control. We caught the shoulder with the rear wheels, and he tried to power us out of danger, but we were lost. We rolled down the slope and ended upside down, turtled, with the motor racing, in complete shock. There were evidently a few other cars in the vicinity that saw us roll. In a minute, I saw some men running up to the car. Neither of us had moved. The good Samaritans were jabbering and were trying desperately to open our doors. They got both front doors open and pulled us out. One of us had evidently cut ourselves because there was some blood, but the site of the injury was not evident. The two men nearest each of us quickly performed a physical exam by feeling our arms and shoulders and obviously asking if we were okay and if it hurt. We seemed to be fine. Willard repeatedly introduced the people to the American expression of "fuck." He was upset. His car was lying on the roof. There was oil leaking from the hood. The windshield had been cracked and popped out. The quarter panel that we had just gotten fixed in Germany was again destroyed, this time extending onto the passenger door. And all of this happened exactly two weeks to the day after the first accident.

The people who stopped for us were very kind and organized the righting of the car. We all stood at one side and pushed it back onto the wheels. It slowly cleared its center of gravity on two wheels and then crashed hard onto the ground. Willard climbed in and after only a couple of tries, it started. We thanked the men and shook all their hands, then turned around, climbed back onto the road, and headed back for the city.

It was comical. The car ran and looked like shit. There were dirt clods and hunks of grass stuck in the windshield and between the hood and the sides. Willard's view was obstructed by the large crack in the windshield, and he was leaning toward me, uttering an incessant string of obscene invectives and "I can't believe it." We didn't have far to drive when, unbelievably, we saw a VW dealership. It was sort of out in the middle of nowhere; we hadn't noticed it on the way out. It looked brand new and was loaded with cars. We drove in and it seemed that every employee came out to see what the problem was. One guy spoke a little English—he was the manager. He was short, fat, bald, smelled bad, had on a cheap-looking suit, and smiled incessantly. Then there was a mechanic-type who spoke a little German. We were trying to talk to both of them at once. The manager left for a moment and came back with an estimate sheet: 13,000 drachmas. We figured it out to over $1,000. It was very depressing as they did not accept Master Charge. We were almost ready to go for it anyway, with the feeling that we had no choice, when the mechanic spoke to us in German. He basically told us about a garage that could fix it for much less downtown. He said to act real mad after discussing the price with the manager so he wouldn't be suspicious that our buddy had told us something. We played it like a couple of vaudevillians and stormed out of there. We kept on driving to town and finally found the garage, really an Esso service station with a VW plaque about six inches long on the side of the wall. It made me think of Steiner's station in Germany. We found another guy who spoke German and told him our sad tale. He was very sympathetic and tried really hard to make us feel better. He did make us feel better when he came back with an estimate of less than 6,000 drachmas. The other good part of this was that they agreed to accept my Esso card. It was perfect. It would not, however, include paint. No problem. We agreed. We also asked why it was so easy to find people who speak German.

"Many of us go to Germany for work. We can make more money there, stay there for a few years, and come back. It is not bad."

He also told us that it would be about three days before the car would be fixed. We hiked back to the hotel. For the rest of our stay we visited local museums, bars, and walked around the city. No further memorable events occurred. When we got the car back, we were all ready to leave. We had decided to drive down to Mount Olympus for a look. It was pretty good. It looked like a real mountain, snowcapped and craggy, coming to a sharp peak. We saw it from a little road beside an orchard of some kind. We were not overcome by any mystic revelations, but we were impressed.

We headed back up to Thessaloniki, for we had driven southwest to get to Mount Olympus. We drove through the city for the last time and got back on the highway. According to our plan, the next stop was Istanbul.

We were in the northern strip of Greece along the upper reaches of the Aegean, south of Bulgaria. There was very little to report. We drove hard for the entire morning, and by noon we were at the Greek-Turkish border. It was formed by a river, and the river was spanned by a long wooden bridge. We drove across the bridge after clearing Greek customs. Before reaching Turkish customs, we saw a duty-free shop on the left side of the end of the bridge. We had a perfect opportunity to supply our alcohol needs in this barren land, so we brought our cash with us and walked up to the window where there was a short line waiting to buy valuable Western goods. It was there that we met George.

CHAPTER 5

We got in line with the few people that were waiting. The sign told us in English, among other tongues, that we could buy two bottles of liquor per person. That seemed fair. We were looking at the selection through the window. The rest of the people in line began to look around behind them, one by one. When we turned around to look ourselves, we saw a remarkable sight. A brand-new Pontiac Grand Prix had pulled up. It was no ordinary Grand Prix, which would have been notable itself. This one was fire-engine red, with a big pimp chrome front end, gangster whitewalls, rabbit-ear antenna protruding from the rear window, and a musical horn that sang as the car parked. Everyone was amazed. The driver stepped out. He had two women with him. He was not tall, brown headed, with a short leather jacket. He walked with a lively step. I could see that one eye was looking off into outer space. I think he was walleyed. He stepped into line behind us and stood there quietly. Within a minute, it was our turn at the window. Predictably, I ordered two bottles of bourbon and Willard ordered two bottles of scotch. We answered no to the question of whether we wanted anything else. We were then surprised to hear our line-mate behind us speak.

"Buy some cigarettes."

"What?"

"Buy some cigarettes," he said.

"But we don't smoke."

"It doesn't matter. We'll take them to Istanbul and sell them on the black market."

Willard and I looked at each other.

"What's the best kind to get?"

"Kent."

So we ordered the maximum number of cartons of Kent cigarettes, two per person.

"Wait for me."

"Sure."

We stepped aside and waited for him to buy his liquor, cigarettes, perfume, silk scarves, two watches, and a fancy pen. He took out a thick packet of $100 traveler's checks and peeled off two. He took his change and walked over to us.

"Come on. I'll buy you guys some lunch. I know a good restaurant up ahead."

"We'll follow you."

We got in our car and followed our friend for about five miles. He turned off down an unpaved road that quickly stopped in front of a drab, grey building. We all got out of our cars.

"I am George. This is my girlfriend, Anna, and her mother, Isabell."

"I'm Bob and this is Bill."

We shook hands all around. George was really something. His smile was infectiously friendly. His misdirected eye seemed to add to his amiability. He talked really fast in a thick accent, Middle Eastern of some kind. His girlfriend was bigger than he was. She was very pretty, but a bit overweight. She spoke Italian with her mother. She and George spoke French with each other. The mother didn't speak French, so George and she spoke Italian. The mother didn't speak English either, so we spoke German with her. We spoke English with Anna, but she also spoke German. I think German was the only language George didn't speak. We all went inside, and George handled everything. In some unrecognizable language, which we presumed to be Turkish, George soon had our table full of lamb, yogurts, bread, tea, coke, and beer. He was right— it was a good restaurant. We ate like pigs. We told George that we were students on a vacation, and that we were heading for Istanbul.

"Good. So are we. I am staying at the Hilton. It is the best Hilton in the world. You guys may not want to stay there, but I can find you a good hotel. Let's go."

Once again, we were following this wild guy down the road. He was hauling ass. It was the first time that I ever saw Willard really working hard to keep up with someone. We did our best. He was passing everybody. I began to wonder about George's eyesight. He was really showing a disregard for oncoming traffic. We made time, though, and were on the outskirts of Istanbul by dusk. A smoky pall hung over the city, and it smelled like burning oil. We pulled up finally to the Hilton. It was beautiful—no, magnificent. The front entrance was spacious and elegant. We parked in the valet parking zone and were met immediately by parking lot attendants. George spoke briefly with one of them, and in less than a minute a distinguished-looking man had come out of the hotel and extended a very warm and gracious welcome to George, complete with bilateral kisses. Willard and I looked at each other with I-guess-this-guy-isn't-so-full-of-shit-after-all looks. George introduced us to him. He was the general manager of the hotel. He handed George a magazine, who then showed it to us. It had a picture of George on the cover. It was the current monthly Hilton magazine. George was dressed in very tight shorts and T-shirt, with a small-billed cap, sitting astride a bicycle, with several gold medals hanging around his neck. We were amazed.

"Let me get settled into our room and then I'll take you to a hotel where I used to stay. It's not too far. It's pretty nice and very cheap."

"You bet, George."

We waited in the lobby for about twenty minutes, and then George appeared.

"Let's go."

We all climbed into the VW and took off. George rode shotgun and gave directions to the Hotel Kennedy. It was a modern-looking, nondescript place wedged in between some apartments. George knew the guy at the desk, and he gave us a special deal on a room. We threw our stuff on the beds and then brought George back to the Hilton.

"We'll go out to dinner tonight, on me. You guys come back here in a couple of hours. Call first and I will meet you in the lobby."

"Okay, George. See you then. Thank you for everything."

He waved good-bye with a smile and walked into the lobby.

"I can't fucking believe this."

"Who is this fucking guy?"

"He's a star. And we're the luckiest guys in the world."

We couldn't stop jabbering for the whole ride back to the Hotel Kennedy. We got to our room and unpacked, then showered and got ready for dinner. The room was modern, but spare. The phone was weird. We kicked back on our beds, and it felt really good.

Then Willard drove us back to the Hilton. We wanted to learn more about George. Obviously, he was a bicycle racer and obviously a good one. No matter what else, he was on the cover of that magazine. George and the two ladies came down to the lobby after we called up.

"Bob . . . Bill."

He called me Bill and Willard Bob as we shook hands. I wasn't sure if it was because he couldn't see us well enough, or because he never got the names straight in the beginning. We said hello to Anna and her mother. We began a truly international conversation in the lobby. I figured that each person could only understand anywhere from twenty to eighty percent of any conversation. It was fun; it felt really cool. George said he knew a fine restaurant. We all climbed into the pimpmobile and drove off. It was great driving with George. It became obvious that he couldn't see worth a shit. I think it was partly because it was dark, and partly because all the other cars had their high beams on. George would alternately hit a siren, the musical horn, or the regular horn when he got in a tight situation or was obstructed by a car or a pedestrian. He was a fearless driver. He was slouched over to the door side of his seat; the seat was pushed all the way back. He had the steering wheel almost horizontal, like a bus. He would look at whoever he was talking to, as best as he could, while weaving through traffic. Maybe he had wider peripheral vision because of his walleye. Even Willard was impressed. George would pass on either side, at any speed. His female acquaintances were bitching the whole time, mostly in Italian. Between the outbursts, he told us that he was Iraqi. I knew that was in the Middle East somewhere. He said he was a bicycling champion, and that he had competed in the Olympics. He was a professional bicycle racer now. He performed marathon races and exhibitions for money. He said he had just finished riding a bicycle for six days straight in Detroit. I asked him how he went to the bathroom, and he said that it was not a problem. He whipped out his traveler's checks and said he had $5,000 worth. He said he had bought the car there and that he was going to sell it for a lot of money. By then we had reached the restaurant. We found our way to a table.

"We'll go back to the hotel later and dance. They have a great disco."

"You bet, George," we said almost in unison. George ordered a large amount of wonderful food: some fish, some lamb, some steak, some unbelievable salad, sauces and bread, and lots of different drinks. It was a feast.

"Where are you traveling, my brudders?" He could not pronounce the "th" sound.

"We don't know, George. We were going to hang around Istanbul for a few days, and then go down the Turkish coast a ways and hop a ferry back to Greece." He screwed up his face and protruded his lower lip a little, nodding slowly.

"You should come to Beirut. It is the most beautiful city in the world. I am going there to sell my car. I told you that. I have an apartment there that you can stay in. There is a store down the street that you can charge beer. It will be wonderful. You should think about it."

"How far away is it?"

"Not too far. You can get there in a few days."

Willard had to be back in America by April 1, and I had to be in Mainz by about the same time. It was January 22.

"I can't think of a reason not to, can you Willard?"

I deferred to his deeper pocket.

"I don't know, T. We're going to run out of money."

"Who is T?"

"It's another name for me."

"No, you are Bill."

I looked at Willard and we both laughed.

"You won't need money in Beirut. I will take care of you."

"We can't let you do that, George."

"Why don't you sell your car, like me? How much did you pay for it?"

"Seventeen hundred dollars."

"You can sell it for twice that in Beirut. I will loan you the money until you sell it."

I looked at Willard and I could see his little wheels turning.

"Maybe we can, George."

We finished the meal. We had a great time. George didn't drink alcohol, but he didn't mind at all if we did. He didn't smoke, but Anna and her mother did. Kents.

"Let's go back to the hotel."

The ride back was wild. George drove us around the city. It was beautiful. We saw the Blue Mosque. Its minarets and domes were illuminated; it didn't look blue. We saw the Golden Horn, a cut of the Sea of Marmara incising the city's center. We saw the Bosporus with its dark oily flow. Mostly we saw masses of people crowding around George's car whenever we stopped at a light or at a corner. He would really get them going with his siren. They jumped. He liked to use it a lot. At first, I thought he was nuts.

"Where are you from, Bob?"

"Reno."

"How about you, Bill?"

"Me too, George."

He nodded again.

"I have been to Las Vegas. I like that city."

We made it back to the Hilton and parked. Several people jumped to the car and opened all the doors. Smiling faces greeted ours. Willard and I were slaphappy. We had certainly seen nice hotels before, but we had to agree with George that this was a good one. It was oriental and elegant. We strode into the lobby behind George, our group once again babbling in about five languages. We were truly being watched by everybody there. We went to the elevator and rode up to the top. It opened up to a spacious area enclosed by glass. There was a spectacular view of the city. George pointed to the side of the city across the water.

"That is Asia over there."

We walked into the disco. It was your basic major hotel, international city, elegant, well-heeled disco. It was pounding out a beautiful female voice who sounded black. The dance floor was packed and moving.

"Dance with Anna, Bob. Tell Bill to dance with her mother. I'll get us a table and drinks."

We all went out and tore it up. Anna was an amazingly good dancer. I didn't really mind that she was fat. Anna's mom was pretty good, too, considering. She was an angry-looking old battle-ax. She wore the heaviest makeup I had ever seen, and her hair was orange blonde. She had very coarse features and deep furrows on her face. But she was really nice. After about five songs, we went looking for George. He had staked out a great big table, and it was loaded with drinks. George was something.

"I thought I told you to dance with Anna, Bob," he said as he was looking at Willard.

"Oh, George, just forget it," said Anna, "that's Bill and that's Bob."

"Okay, Bob. I got it, Bill."

We all laughed.

"I can't believe we met you, George. Hey, how many languages do you speak anyway?"

"Seven. Arabic, Turkish, Armenian, French, English, Italian, and Spanish. Some others too."

"Where's Iraq?"

"Between Syria and Iran."

"What's it like?"

"It is a beautiful country. Very poor. Very old. You would like it."

"What are you going to do after you sell your car?"

He hesitated. "I don't know, brudder."

Anna lifted up her chin slowly while keeping her eyes on him as he said that. She smiled when she saw me looking at her.

"When you come to Beirut, I will really show you a good time. There is no place like it. Casinos, discos, banks, restaurants. Everything is wonderful. I know you will come."

Willard and I laughed. We decided to ask some girls at another table to dance. They were from someplace really different; I couldn't tell where. They were pretty good dancers but flirted and laughed with each other through the whole song. They dashed back the very second the song ended. We wandered back to the table.

"What do you say we go now? I have some business tomorrow. Call me tomorrow night."

We said good night to George and the ladies and watched them leave. George had told the waiter to charge all our drinks to his room. We accepted his hospitality with gusto. It was wild. A whole group of girls rolled in. I think they were from Switzerland or Germany. We danced with almost every one. I got a kiss from one of them. I think Willard was trying to feel another's tits. We were shit-faced. It was 3:00 a.m., and we were beat. We said our good-byes and stumbled out. Thank God the Hotel Kennedy was not far or hard to find. We made it back without a hitch and crashed in our beds.

We did some sightseeing the next day. Istanbul is an amazing place. We saw so many things that we had never seen before. I saw a dancing bear with a gypsy. There were squalid wooden buildings that looked like they had been fashionable residences in times past. We saw massive mosques and churches. Everywhere there were hordes of people. The predominant car was a black '57 Chevy with black-and-yellow checkerboard around the front and back ends; these were the cabs. We started out in the area of the Hilton. Around it was a teeming cosmopolitan city with every variety of retail store and shop. We were accosted by numerous black-market purveyors of cigarettes and were reminded that we needed to bring our cigarettes to the marketplace. One fellow offered us hash, but we declined. Maybe later. We crossed the Galata Bridge by foot to the Old City. It was old. There was a large mosque at the end of the bridge. It was ironically called the New Mosque. There was a large square next. We stopped for a fine meal of kabob and beer. We hiked around the Old City. Whatever feelings of strangeness that I felt in Europe paled. Every now and then I would see an attractive female, and she would be incessantly prodded and hassled by every man who walked by. What a place!

We both wanted to take a Turkish bath, so we asked the first man who looked like he spoke English. He did. He told us that the best one in the city was close by and gave us simple directions that led us around two corners and placed us in front of another drab, grey building. We entered the door and paid a small amount of money for towels and entrance to the bath. We then were led into an anteroom that was warm, but not hot. Then we walked into the bath itself. It was a tall, vaulted stone room with holes in the ceiling. Shafts of light like sunlight burning through a thundershower lit the steamy air. Dark, hairy men wrapped in towels about the waist were lying or sitting on the floor. It was difficult to breathe at first, but soon we melted onto the floor with the others. It was a total experience. We met an old Turkish businessman who suggested that we get a massage. We did. After being cooked and tenderized, we retrieved our clothes and oozed out of the bath. I hadn't felt that good after a workout since I had lifted weights.

We made our way back out of the Old City and over the bridge. We returned to our home base, the Hilton. As we entered the lobby, we saw George. He was sitting in a lounge drinking coffee with some men wearing unusual headgear: patterned cloth with small tassels, wrapped completely around the head and neck. We just watched them for a minute and decided not to interrupt. George seemed angry, even frightened, as he spoke, or maybe he was just especially animated. The other men sat quietly and said very little. Willard and I looked at each other and did not know what to make of it all, so we got in our car and drove back to the other hotel for a nap.

We rang up George's room and Anna answered it.

"I have not seen George since this morning."

"He said to call him tonight."

"Oh, Bob, here he comes now." He came on the phone.

"I just got back from a meeting across town. I am very tired right now. Would you mind if we skipped tonight? I will call you in the morning, and I will show you the city. We will go shopping. What do you want to buy?"

"We were thinking about buying leather coats. We heard that they are really cheap here."

"You hear right, Bob. We'll go shopping tomorrow. *Adieu.* Go over to the Passage of the Flowers to eat. You'll like it. Be careful. Do not do any black-market sales without me. It can be a dangerous city, brudder."

Once again, we didn't know quite what to think. But we showered and drove again to the Hilton to park the car. We walked down the main drag and found our way to the street George had told us about. It was really an alley. It was loaded with people, milling and singing and shouting, moving as a single large amorphous organism down the cobblestone. We turned into a restaurant and sat down to another fabulous meal of lamb and beer, with plenty of condiments. We were sitting next to an old, toothless man who smiled constantly but did not speak English or German. We became friends nonetheless. We bought him a few beers and he was most appreciative. We drank beer until he called for ouzo. We poured the clear liquor into glasses half filled with mineral water. The mixture would immediately turn cloudy white. It tasted like black licorice and was not really that good, but it did work well. We were learning songs from our friend. As things began to wind down, he shook our hands and bade his farewell. I stood up and inquired in the international sign language, with my hands placed parallel to each other in front of me describing an hourglass shape: Where are the women? He laughed loudly and grabbed my arm. Willard followed somewhat reluctantly, and we were soon in tow. We walked for at least a mile, winding down lower and lower through completely black streets and alleys. I was too drunk to be suspicious. Willard was bringing up the rear, constantly chiding me.

"Where are we going, T? This guy could be taking us to hell for all we know."

Our friend smiled on. We finally seemed to reach our destination. It was another squalid building. At the door, our friend arranged for our entrance, and we entered a smoky hall full of men and whining, undulating music, just like you might expect in Turkey. There was a belly dancer working the crowd. She was good and had little finger cymbals and silk veils. She spotted us and began to dance her way over to our table. She had her torso in Willard's face. Our friend spoke to her, and she slipped off her veil. She was pretty, but then when she opened her mouth it was sort of anticlimactic; her teeth were half gone, and the remaining ones were blackened and broken. Oh well. Willard and I were laughing and clapping to the music. The rest of the crowd was amused by the American boys, and one of the guys behind us pushed Willard up out of his seat, into the dancer. She laughed and rubbed closer into Willard. He immediately loosened up and started undulating into her. I was laughing my ass off. She finally wove her body away from our table, and Willard sat down after I grabbed his shirt and pulled him back.

"This is great, T, but let's get the fuck out of here."

I gave the thumbs-out sign to our buddy, and he laughed heartily as he led us out of the bar. We walked away into the night; we hoped that we were being led back to the original restaurant. After another really long walk, we found ourselves at the Passage of Flowers again. We hugged our friend and thanked him profusely. He smiled and laughed, slapped us on our backs, and staggered off. We did the same in the other direction, to our car, and once again wound our way back to the Hotel Kennedy and our beds.

CHAPTER 6

We were awakened by an unmusical clack, like a bell loose on its screw. Neither of us knew what it was until Willard picked up the phone and the grating noise stopped.

"Wake up, Bob. We are going to the market to buy the things that you want. Come over and we will meet you in the lobby here."

We showered and dressed, grabbing sips of dark, viscous coffee on the run as we went through the lobby of the Hotel Kennedy. The clerk behind the desk asked us if we would be seeing George today. When I answered yes, he told me to tell him that his bicycle was ready.

We raced to the Hilton and parked with the valet. George was already in the lobby.

"Where are Anna and her mother?"

"They are busy with packing."

"Are you leaving, George?"

"We all are. We are going to Ankara."

"Where the hell is that?"

"It is on the way to Beirut."

He moved past us and snapped his fingers as he went through the front doors. Willard and I looked at each other, shrugged our shoulders, and followed him to his car, which was obviously being held ready in waiting.

"When are we leaving?"

"Tomorrow. But first we have to get you some leather coats. We will go to the Covered Bazaar. You won't believe it. We will find exactly what you want, for much less than you think we can buy it for. Listen and watch and do not say too much. I will show you how to buy in the Middle East."

We drove out of the hotel lot and turned into the busy front street.

"By the way, George, the guy at the Hotel Kennedy said that your bicycle is ready."

His head stopped. We were in the middle of negotiating a corner to the left, and he continued the turn, even more blindly than usual, with his head facing now to the right. I could see his walleye seeking me, trying to see me and assess my face to corroborate or disbelieve my remark. I don't think that the eye could see much; the pose and tone of his head were more like smelling, sniffing the air for clues.

"I have too many bikes. I wonder which one he means."

"I don't know; he didn't say. Do you want me to ask him?"

"I will ask him when I go over there with you tonight."

We crossed the Galata Bridge into the Old City. After a short ride, George pulled up to what appeared to be an entrance of some kind, turned on his siren, waited for a small crowd to gather, and parked. He got two young boys to watch the car for a pittance each, and we walked into the market. This was another Istanbul experience. Large alleyways choked with people between shops of innumerable types and number lay before us. We followed George; he seemed to know where he was going. We saw signs, clocks, street vendors, and the widest spectrum of

38

commodities I had ever seen. Every other shop seemed to be a jewelry store. George turned into a drably fronted store with a dirty picture window. Inside was a small cavern lined with leather coats.

"Look around; see if there is something that you like."

We looked, but most of the coats were short jackets or half-length coats, mostly glossy leather in blacks and browns.

"These are nice, George, but we were looking for something more exotic. Something suede, or goatskin, with fur and beads and embroidery. You know, like from Afghanistan or something."

He shook his head and turned to the storekeeper. They spoke earnestly with each other, and the storekeeper pointed some directions to George. George thanked him, we waved our thanks, and then moved out of the store and into the teeming streets. Again we followed George, and again we entered a dingy storefront.

"*Marhaba*," he said to the shopkeeper.

"Look around," he said to us.

This was the place. It was larger than the last, another cavern of leather, rows of coats and jackets hanging stacked to the ceiling, four deep in some places. There was one whole corner of hats, furry Russian-looking ones, and fedoras, and the soft kind with a firm bill that attaches to the main part by a button—the kind that they wear among the European peasantry. We looked at each other then began a serious search. I must have tried on fifty coats, and Willard did the same. We each had one of the shopkeepers at our sides. George was close by, and offered his opinion on the look, and told us what the price was for each coat of interest. He was not speaking Turkish with the men; that much I knew. I guessed it to be Arabic. He was very quiet except when we asked him specific questions. The men spoke almost incessantly to each other the whole time. I wondered if George could understand what they were saying. I was sure he could.

Many of the coats went into four figures and were beautiful; we could tell which ones were out of our reach. Willard found a great one, though. It was white suede, three-quarter length, with lamb's wool around the wrist cuffs and collar. It had what looked to be hand-embroidered brocade on the back in an oriental pattern. The inside was lined entirely with the same lamb's wool as the cuffs and collar. I could tell that he wanted it bad. I also found the right one. Mine was full length, brown suede, with fur lining going out to a large, broad collar that could fold up to engulf my whole head. We each found hats that seemed to have been made for our coats, thick furry cylinders of exactly the same color as our coats.

"These are the ones, George; how much?"

George talked to the men and turned to us.

"Yours is five hundred dollars, Bill, and yours is seven hundred."

By now we knew that he had our identities indelibly reversed; I was glad that Willard's was more.

"How much do you think we can get them down, George?"

"Watch me, and don't say another word. Do exactly as I say."

He was firm, almost angry as he spoke, but with absolute calmness. He turned slowly to the men and started to haggle. This was serious. George was holding his own against both of them. They weren't sure when he was looking at them or away from them, or even which one he was looking at. I'm sure that this threw them off. In between they would talk to each other in what I guessed was Turkish. They seemed to be arguing with each other at those times. George reached a certain level of intensity with them and then leveled off. He continued on this plateau for a very short time, then suddenly said, "They want six hundred dollars for both of them."

"Take it, George."

"No, they'll go lower. I want them both for four hundred and fifty."

"Don't fuck around, George. We want these coats."

He looked at Willard with a cold, brutal stare, and Bill froze.

George said about five more words, then suddenly turned to us and said, "Let's go."

We followed him out and as soon as we got out of the door, we assaulted him.

"Goddammit, George, we want those coats. What the fuck are you doing? I'll never get another chance at something like that."

Willard was pissed. I wasn't so sure.

"Shut your mouth, keep walking, and don't look back."

He almost scared me with his voice. We walked quietly down the street for about fifty feet. Suddenly, behind us, I heard the voices of the shopkeepers yelling after us. George grabbed Willard's hand when he tried to turn around, and we walked another twenty feet. The voices grew louder and more frantic. I felt a hand grab my shoulder. I feared the worst. I looked straight ahead. George turned slowly around to face the wheezing shopkeeper, nodded to his entreaty, then looked at Bill as he said, "We have them for four fifty."

"How in the fuck did you do that, George? I mean, really, how did you do it? How did you know?"

We walked back to the shop, and George made the purchase with traveler's checks. We had our coats bundled up in grease cloth and twine and tucked them under our arms as we walked down the covered street. Willard was walking next to George, facing him and walking sideways as he questioned him.

"I spoke Arabic with them, and they did not know that I spoke Turkish. I made myself sound like a man who only spoke a small dialect of Arabic, and nothing else. They had a very interesting discussion in Turkish. They have a large note due in three days, and they are very short of money. They would have accepted anything that we offered. I was being kind by offering four fifty."

George walked on, just a little ahead of us. We looked at each other and laughed out loud. George turned around, looked us over, and shook his head. We got back to the car, and the boys had washed it. George gave them more change and we climbed in.

"We're really sorry we were so stupid, George."

"You almost ruined my plan. Maybe next time you will trust me."

We got back to the Hilton and wore our coats upstairs to show off to Anna and her mother. They loved the coats and told us what a great deal we had made.

"You mean what a great deal George made."

"I am not surprised," Anna said.

We took off our coats and lounged around George's suite. He decided to send out for room service for supper. Needless to say, it was another fabulous meal. We finished the meal and moved to the sofa.

"We are going out."

"Where are you going?"

"I don't know. Come on Bob, Bill. I will be back later."

George and Willard and I left the suite and got them to bring his car around. We drove off.

"Would you like to go out with some girls tonight?"

"Sure, George."

"I know two sisters that would love to meet you. I will leave you there and come back for you later."

We drove across town to an old residential area, and George pointed out a doorway.

"Go ring the bell and I will see you later. Have fun."

We did as he said. A thirtyish woman answered the door.

"You must be Bob and Bill. Please come in. I am Aliye. My sister Cela is above." She pointed upstairs. She spoke haltingly in a heavy accent and gestured us into the sitting room.

"Would you like to drink?"

"Yes, thank you. I am Bob and this is Bill."

Aliye was not attractive. She had a nice body, but her face was rough with rather bad acne. Her sister came downstairs; she was cuter, but mildly obese.

"Yours ain't looking too good," I smiled to Willard through the side of my mouth. Aliye had brought us mineral water and a bottle of ouzo, or something like it. Her sister did not speak English. We decided to drink heavily. It was slightly awkward. The sisters did not drink, could not talk, looked pretty bad, and had hairy armpits and legs. Even a moderate level of intoxication didn't help their attractiveness much. They played some terrible lounge-lizard-type music and began to dance with each other. Willard and I started to dance with each other. It was a ludicrous sight. We finally switched partners; I ended up with fatso. We were slow dancing, each rotating slowly around our respective partners. Willard smiled widely to me while we faced each other. As I rotated away from him, I saw Cela's smile quickly erode into a frown, and she began to well up with tears. I rotated around to face Willard again, and he was smiling and waving to me with one hand. I didn't understand why Cela was upset until I craned my head around and saw Willard giving her the universal sign of his finger penetrating in and out within a circle formed by his thumb and forefinger of the other hand. Nice guy. I stroked her head and shook my head sympathetically. By now her sister was laughing with Willard, so I started laughing. Cela walked away into the kitchen. I sat down on the couch and watched as Willard was trying to get something going; I had seen that movie before. I continued to drink the wretched ouzo. Willard and Aliye locked hands and walked upstairs.

About an hour passed and then the phone rang. Cela came downstairs. I guess she had gotten upstairs from the other side of the kitchen.

Aliye came down next and said that Bill would come soon. I had to laugh. She told me that George was coming over to get us. Bill came downstairs.

"You dickhead."

"What do you mean?"

Cela interrupted, "You should wait outside, George said. It was good to meet you. I am sorry for my sister."

"It's okay; she was the only one with any sense."

We shook their hands, said good-bye, and walked into the street. George's car was waiting at the corner, and we climbed in.

"How did it go?"

"They were pigs, George."

"I know. I am sorry. It was the best I could do for you on short notice. Was it better than nothing?"

"I don't know. Ask Bill. Mine was nothing."

"I didn't do anything either."

"You lying sack of shit. You fucked that pig."

"No way."

I shook my head at Willard. George laughed. After a minute we were all laughing.

"How did you do, George?"

"What do you mean?"

"I know you did better than we did."

"I went and saw the bike that the hotel man told you about. I do not need it right now. He is going to keep it for me."

"Right, George." We laughed some more.

We pulled into the Hilton, and George had his car parked. He called for ours.

"Be here early tomorrow and we will drive to Ankara. It is not nice like Istanbul, but we will have fun. I will bring your coats. Get a good night's sleep."

We returned for the last time to the Hotel Kennedy and turned in. We would pack our few things in the morning.

CHAPTER 7

It was cold. The weather had turned overnight. It felt like winter for the first time since Yugoslavia. We inched our way through some heavy traffic before we broke through and made some time on our way to the Hilton. We pulled into the parking area and parked to the side, witnessing a flurry of activity around George's car. Valets were unloading George's things off a rack into his car. The grand poobah of a general manager was pointing in every direction of the compass, unnecessarily directing his underlings. Then George arrived with his entourage of Anna and her mother, followed by bellmen carrying a few things. I assumed our coats to be in two bulky, plastic garment bags. George saw us and came over.

"Are you ready, Bill?"

"We're ready, George. It sure got cold all of a sudden."

"It is winter. We will see snow before the day is over."

George didn't have snow tires, but somehow I didn't think that would slow him down. He told the bellmen to bring the garment bags to our car, and we laid them flat in the back of the rear section. The coffee man from the lobby had brought us out some libation, which really tasted good. George oversaw the organization of his departure and kissed the GM twice for old time's sake. His car was finally loaded with his people and his things. He walked around to us.

"Ankara is only a few hundred miles, but it is a difficult road through the mountains. There is no need to hurry. You can follow me. I will let you know when we should stop. Are you ready to go to Beirut?"

"We're ready, George. Let's hit it."

We followed George down the street and saw that we were heading to the Galata Bridge. We crossed it and turned at the other end into a small parking lot. This was the ferry station, and we were in line for one that George had picked out. Vendors of food and drink came by and offered their goods. I saw a group of cars move to the front of our line. George told us that they were a wedding party.

"Funerals and weddings go to the front. I think the reason is that they both are the end of the line."

We got to board the ferry in a few minutes. I was excited. Next stop, Asia. We munched on sandwiches and drank coffee as the boat pulled away in a lurch of smoke and rumbling engines. The air was very brisk and clear; it was coming from somewhere other than Istanbul. We plowed through the little whitecaps. I looked back at the European part of the city and felt the thrill of impending strangeness come to me again.

"Here we go again, Willard," I yelled through the noise and wind. He laughed and nodded his head in agreement. The ride was a short one. The captain nosed us into our berth, and we climbed back into our cars. We followed George off the boat. He took off down the street. I guess he really didn't mean it when he said we would be in no hurry. Once again, he seemed to know where he was going. We were blasting down boulevards and weaving through narrow streets full of traffic and pedestrians. George was giving his siren a good workout.

Istanbul is a big city. It was a long time before we were on the highway—a narrow, chuckholed little road full of trucks and ancient cars. George was true to form, passing at will, wantonly challenging any vehicle heading in either direction. Willard was working harder than ever to keep up. The countryside was nondescript, low and flat with trees clumped at the edge of pastures outlined with stone walls. The horizon showed us mountains with clouds tethered to the peaks, a definitely wintry view. I shivered as I thought of crossing these in the middle of winter with George as our guide. We began to go uphill. The scenery became more familiar-looking. It looked like Nevada in the wintertime: high clouds racing before a cold wind, dodging rough, rocky hills and mountain passes; tumbleweeds rolling and collecting on fence lines; snow in the distance covering the upper slopes of brown-to-black crags. At least we knew what was in store for us geographically and weather wise. We approached a small town. Anna turned around and signaled to us that we would be stopping.

We stopped at a restaurant, and George ordered lunch for us. It was typically wonderful with the usual variety. George spoke with the owner and apparently, they talked about the weather.

"It is snowing up ahead."

"We could have told you that, George. This is just like Nevada. It's snowing right now in those mountains."

"We will make it to Ankara tonight, but it will be dark before we get there. There is really no place to spend the night."

"We'll be fine, George."

Anna, Willard, and I all looked at each other with incredulous faces. We pressed on.

We started seeing snow falling after going through Adapazari, a pretty good-sized town. George really slowed down. We could tell that he had no clue about driving in the snow. The ass end of his car would drift around curves, and he used his brakes all the time. It was already getting hard to see even though it was only early afternoon. The light was flat, and the snow started to swirl in the wind. Willard and I were doing pretty good; the VW had reasonable traction and we were enjoying the show that George was putting on for us. It really began to snow hard. George had on his lights, wipers, brakes, and anything else he could turn on trying to see where the hell he was going.

Darkness settled in very quickly. There was still a lot of traffic on the road. The drivers in Turkey turn on their high beams and leave them on. We tried flashing our lights at the first few cars, but it soon became obvious that they had no interest in our message. George was really having a hard time. It was damn near impossible for us to see, and I was sure George was driving by Braille. We could see him almost run off the road as he would continually recorrect his path. I was really concerned.

"Let's tell him that one of us will drive his car, Willard. This is getting scary."

"He won't let anyone else drive."

I had to agree. Fortunately, we saw George put on his blinker. He had seen a small building off the road and pulled into the gravelly lot. There were quite a few cars parked; they were all covered with snow. Anna stepped out of the car, wrapped in a full-length fur coat. She was obviously very pissed off at George. She yelled at him in Italian and walked over to us.

"He is crazy. I will not ride with him anymore. Can I and my mother ride with you?"

"Sure, Anna. But don't you think that one of us can drive George's car instead?"

"He will not even think of it. I told you that he is crazy. He is crazy in all things. You do not know how crazy he is."

George had come up behind Anna as she finished her remarks. He grabbed her from behind, by the nape of the neck, and turned her around toward the building.

"We are going to have some coffee."

We trudged to the building, and George pushed open the door. We followed him in single file, milling about at the entrance, shaking off the cold and the snow. I closed the door behind us and sealed out the weather. We had entered a coffeehouse. There must have been fifty men sitting around drinking tea and coffee and smoking cigarettes. Now, I've walked into black bars in Houston, bars for sailors in Galveston, Irish bars in South Boston, and Basque bars in Nevada, but I never felt so alone and out of place as I did here. Each man had stopped speaking and stared at us, mostly fixing their gaze on Anna. George was cool. He uttered something in Turkish, and a short, bald man with a cigarette hanging from his lips and rolled-up sleeves ushered us to a table. Shortly, the man brought us a tray with five coffees, five teas, and three cokes in bottles. George didn't say a word to Anna or her mother. He was his usual jovial self to us.

"This is not a good place to be."

We played along, smiling quietly and looking only at George. The coffeehouse was hospital green with a small tiled stove in the back. It was cloudy with smoke. The tables were topped with what looked like old linoleum, so worn that the central part of each table was denuded of the color; so gradually did it arrive in that state that there was no palpable demarcation line between the colored and worn areas. Each man was drinking coffee or tea from a small clear glass on a saucer. I did not see any ashtrays.

"We should not even be driving at night up here. The hills are full of bandits, and they would slit our throats and take Anna in a second."

He looked at Anna and laughed.

"We will finish our drinks and go."

"Why don't you let one of us drive your car, George. It's really hard to see out there, and we're used to driving in the snow. We've both done it for years."

"No thanks, Bill. We're not that far from Ankara. I will leave some money for this man. You and Bob get up after that and escort the ladies to the door. I will follow you out."

We did as he said and walked the ladies out to the cars. It had almost stopped snowing. That was a relief. I looked and didn't see any footprints around our cars other than the ones we had made. That was also a relief. George came out after about thirty seconds.

"Let's go."

You didn't have to tell us twice. We led the way out of the lot onto the highway, and George was close on our tail. This was much better. Now George only had to see our taillights. Even he could do that.

The rest of the ride into Ankara was uneventful. Willard took it easy. We hit another patch of flurries and a few spots of very slippery roadway. We couldn't see that well ourselves with George's high beams reflecting off the rearview mirror into our eyes, but it wasn't that bad. We dropped down out of a pass and saw a large city ahead of us, miles in the distance. George passed us on the first straight section. We followed him into Ankara. Once again, he seemed to know where he was going. He led us through the city to a nice, big hotel. We pulled in and got out in the parking area.

"We can all stay here tonight. It's not a bad place. We've earned a good night's sleep."

The bellman loaded up our things and we checked in. George got us a room next to his suite. We all said good night to each other. Anna gave us both a hug. Willard and I were whipped; we fell into our beds and passed out.

We slept in until about ten. It was just what we needed. I woke up and went out in the hall; I thought I had heard George's voice. He was standing in his doorway with a razor in his hand, shaving his dry face.

"How did you sleep, Bill?"

"I slept fine, George. How about you guys?"

"Not too bad."

"Doesn't that hurt your face, George? Where I come from, dry shaving is a form of torture."

"This does not hurt. Where I come from, we have much better forms of torture."

George and I went down into the lobby. It was not the Istanbul Hilton, but it was a nice tourist hotel. We bought some coffee and sat down.

"Have you guys been having a good time?"

"We're having the time of our lives, George. I can't believe we met you. You have been very kind to us."

"You are not the only ones who are lucky. If it weren't for you two, I would be stuck with Anna and her mother. It has been good for all of us. But it is nothing compared to the fun that we will have in Beirut. I cannot tell you enough about that city. It is the most beautiful city in the world. Everything is there. We will eat like kings, and I will show you everything. I have many friends there. You will see."

"How far away are we now?"

"Only a few more days. But we have to make . . . some plans." He hesitated. "We will have to split up for a while."

"What do you mean?"

"I cannot go into Syria from Turkey. It is because I am Iraqi. The border there is difficult for me to pass. You will have no problem. I will have to go to Cyprus, and from there travel to Syria. It is the only way."

"We can go with you, George. We don't have to split up."

"I don't think so. I have some business there, and I won't have time for any fun. I have some plans for you guys, some friends for you to meet, and I will see you in Damascus. Then we will drive to Beirut together. Don't worry. Come on. Let's see if anyone else is awake."

We went up to George's suite. Willard was there, and Anna and her mother were working on their suitcases. I looked outside and it was clear. There was no snow in Ankara, but it looked cold and crisp. People were dressed for winter.

"Who is hungry?"

Willard and I looked at each other. We had both gotten fat as shit. It was the off-season for me from football. During the season, I had a hard time keeping my weight up to 210 pounds, even with big meals and weight training. Now I easily weighed 220, and it was junk. I hadn't exercised in six weeks. Willard was not tall and inclined to have thick thighs and a big ass. He looked like a little bowling ball.

"We are."

"Let's go."

We did lunch in our usual grand manner. George had found another fabulous restaurant. It took him about thirty seconds before the management of any establishment began to treat him like a combination of family and royalty. His friendliness was irresistible. He complemented that with an air of importance and impetuousness. He snapped his fingers while he walked and while he waited. It was like a timer, and everyone with whom he dealt was on the clock. Things happened when George was there. Every meal, every shopping experience, every situation was extreme. George was always pushing it. I don't think he slept very much.

We went back to the hotel after lunch and took a nap. I was beat. Willard was always good for a nap. While we lay there, we talked.

"George says we have to split up for a while."

"Whaddya mean?"

"He can't get into Syria from Turkey, some kind of problem because he's Iraqi. He has to go to Cyprus, then into Syria from there. He wants us to go to Damascus."

"Why can't we go with him?"

"He says that he's got business."

"What business? I've never seen him do one bit of business. He's full of shit. He's gonna go party somewhere. I'm surprised he isn't sending Anna and her mother with us."

"I think he is."

"What?"

"Just kidding."

"What the hell are we going to do in Damascus? How far is it?"

"He said it's not too far. He has some friends there that he wants us to look up, then he'll meet us there in a few days."

"Oh."

George woke us up and told us to get dressed. I guess George wanted to party. We went to his suite. It was full of food, drinks, people, music, and a belly dancer. I couldn't fucking believe it—where did all these people come from? They were wild looking. The guys were really dark with scruffy dark beards, disco clothes, smoked cigarettes, the whole bit.

"Who are these people, George?"

"Some friends of mine."

Willard and I looked at each other. Right. They had some weird kind of liquor there, so I went next door and got a bottle of Jack Daniel's that I still had from the Greek-Turkish border. Then Willard went and got his bottle of Cutty. We set the bottles out and the locals glommed on real fast. I taught a few of them how to play cardinal puff. They were admittedly at some disadvantage because of the language issue, but they were pitiful. They giggled like little girls and really got fucked up on hardly any booze. Not one of them cleared even the first hurdle toward becoming a cardinal. They all eyed the belly dancer lasciviously and tried to establish eye contact like hard dicks at a whorehouse. I talked to Anna for a while.

"Why is George going to Cyprus?"

"He cannot get into Syria from here."

"Why not?"

"I do not know exactly."

"He said we can't go with you to Cyprus."

"I know."

"Why is that?"

"Please, Bob, ask George. I really don't know."

She was not upset with me for asking, but she was unable to answer me. There was a little desperation in her voice.

"I'm sorry, Anna. I didn't mean to upset you or ask questions I shouldn't."

"It's not that, Bob. It's just that you should talk to George about these things. I really do not know the answers to your questions."

Back to the giggly Turks or whatever they were. One of them was throwing up in the bathroom. He was a real squirrelly bastard. I laughed. Then I saw that the JD was almost gone. Oh well. Willard was dancing with the dancer. He was really something. He had a huge smile on his face. George was laughing his ass off. His friends were in a circle around them clapping to the music. They wanted Willard to take off his shirt. I begged God that he would not do it. He did it. His gut was huge. I resorted to the last of the JD. George came up to the table for a drink.

"Want some whiskey, George?"

"I'll have a little, thank you, Bill."

"Now, why can't we go with you to Cyprus, again?"

"You can if you want, but you will have more fun in Damascus. There is nothing on Cyprus, and I will be busy."

"Would you mind if I asked you what you do for business?"

"No, not at all. I work for an organization that supports Middle Eastern people."

"Oh."

"I have some name and influence because of my bicycle racing, and I help with public relations and communication. It is nothing serious, but I like to do it. There are many problems in the Middle East, and I do a little bit to help my people."

"Who are your people, the Iraqis?"

"Them, the Armenians, and the Palestinians."

"I've heard of the Palestinians, but I don't know much about them. Who are they?"

"You are not told of their side in the United States. We will talk more of them."

George wandered off into the party. It was clear to me that he was a very interesting and deep man.

The party continued, predictably, until the booze was gone and there had been several more entries in the porcelain bus-driving competition. I was glad the party was in George's room. Anna and her mother were long since in bed. George finally told the hard core that they had to leave; they very kindly obliged. The spokesman for the group made a little speech.

"You are with a good man, my friends. He is a good soldier. He will take care of you."

George whispered in his ear as he ushered him out the door. I started to pick up some of the trash.

"Go to bed. Leave this shit. Good night, my friends."

"Good night, George."

CHAPTER 8

I awoke from dreams of Beirut. It was very bizarre. We had sold our car for ten thousand dollars to the president of Lebanon. He had let us stay in his palace. George was his buddy, and we had the run of the country. It seemed like a great place. I woke instead to Willard having a conniption fit. I witnessed his performing a burp, fart, sneeze, and cough at the same instant.

"Gimme a fucking break, would you."

"Shit, I don't know what happened."

"Your brain and body are liquefying and turning to garbage."

"Shut up."

We got out of bed.

"I'm using the bathroom first. You're disgusting." I was laughing uncontrollably.

"Fuck you."

I went out in the hall after I was showered, etc., and found George in his usual position, dry shaving in the hall.

"Do you shave this way every day, George? Believe it or not, water makes it easier."

"I don't have time for water."

I will say this about George: his hygiene was amazingly good. He didn't stink like many of the third world people I'd met.

"What's up for today?"

"I think we go separate ways today."

"Oh."

"We will talk about it over lunch."

Anna came to the door.

"Good morning, Anna."

"Good morning, Bob."

"I know he is Bill."

"Please, George."

He went back into his room.

"George says we're going to split up today."

"I know."

"Will we see you again?"

"Of course." She was shocked that I would ask that question.

"Just checking."

"George loves you two. He would never do anything to hurt you. We will see you in Beirut. Everything that he has said is true. We will have the best time."

"I know we will."

Willard had come out and greeted Anna She returned it warmly, and then Willard got down to business.

"What's for breakfast?"

"You're so fucking gross."

"When we get to Beirut, I will make you some very good food. I cannot cook for you until I get there. My mother is even better as a cook."

I believed her.

We returned to our rooms and got our few things together to travel.

"We're splitting up today," I said to Willard.

"I figured as much."

"What do you think this is all about?"

"I have no fucking idea, but I'm not worried. I trust George."

"So do I. He wouldn't fuck us."

"No, he wouldn't."

We went to George's room, but they had already gone downstairs. We went to the lobby as George was checking out. Anna and her mother came to us.

"George wants to have a special lunch. He is asking the clerk where is the best restaurant in Ankara."

Needless to say, we found the place. Needless to say, it was unbelievable.

"We need to talk about the next few days."

"We know."

"The way to Damascus is not hard. It is the main road south. There is really only one way. The weather will start to get warmer as you get near the Mediterranean. It will only take you a few days to get there. There is not much between here and there. The border crossing into Syria will not be hard for you. You are Americans. When you get to Damascus, go to Hotel Gondola. It is run by an old friend of mine, Abu Adnah. He has some of my bicycles. Tell him that you are friends of mine, and he will take care of you. Tell him that I will be arriving in a few days. I cannot say exactly when I will be there, but wait for me."

"We don't have much choice, George. Of course we'll wait for you. If you can't come for us, we are really fucked. There is no way we are going to drive back to Germany. Are you sure we can sell my car for a good price? We're going to run out of money pretty soon, and if we don't, we're really going to be stuck."

ROBERT TIBOLT

"Listen to me, Bob. I promise you that I will come for you in Damascus. You do not have to worry about this. Your car we will certainly sell for much more than you bought it. Remember that I am taking my car to Beirut for the same reason. And also remember that Beirut is the most beautiful city in the world," he turned his head toward Anna, "with the most beautiful women in the world. Let me tell you more. I have an apartment in Beirut that you can have for as long as you want. Money is not a problem. I will loan you whatever money that you need, and your car will certainly cover all of your expenses there. I just want you guys to go to Beirut."

"Well, we're going there, George. Just don't fuck us."

"I told you last time at the market that you had to trust me; I thought you might have learned your lesson."

"We trust you all the way, George. That's why we're going to Beirut."

"Which way are you going, George?"

"I am going the same way, and we can travel together for a while today. Then I turn to the south. I need to reach the city of Silifke, and you need to go into Syria. We both need to leave now. One last thing. I will give you the telephone number of my apartment in Beirut. You can reach my friends there at the White House Apartments if you need to."

He scribbled down a telephone number and gave it to me. I said my good-bye to Anna and her mother, and so did Bill. We were a little sad, but not as sad as Anna.

"We'll see you real soon, Anna. We can't wait until we eat some of your great food."

"I will make you the best food, and you will love everything. Don't worry about George; you will see him again soon."

We each climbed into our cars and headed out of town. The weather was clear and cool. George made great time, and we kept up. After only a few minutes, George pulled over at a crossroads. He stopped and got out of his car. We got out.

"Take this road all the way to Syria. First you will reach Adana in Turkey. Then follow the road to Syria. I must turn here and go to the coast for a ferry to Cyprus. Take good care, my brudders. I will see you soon. Oh, and if I can't see you in Damascus, meet me in Beirut." He gave us each a hug and a kiss, Arab style. We waved to the ladies in the car, climbed into ours, and watched George race off into the distance.

CHAPTER 9

George's red pimpmobile soon faded into a black speck that vanished into the dark hills of central Turkey. There were no other cars. We looked around in silence. It was really reminiscent of Nevada now—the quiet and solitude were infinite. We knew we were alone.

"That was fun."

"Whose idea was it to go to Beirut anyway?"

"What did he mean by, 'If I can't see you in Damascus, meet me in Beirut?'"

"I have no fucking idea. You know George."

We both laughed as Willard revved up the VW and peeled off onto the highway. We didn't say much to each other. We didn't have enough confidence in what we were doing to talk about it. We were getting farther away from Germany with every minute, with no guarantee of any reasonable way of getting back. I turned on a tape. We made good time across the high desert. We passed a huge lake on our right and saw marshes that were totally devoid of any waterfowl. Later, we passed a pretty good-sized mountain on our left that was craggy and snow-covered. There was little else to notice. The monotony and seeming familiarity of the terrain somehow began to soothe my feelings of fear, and I soon felt more excited and less lonely and afraid. I was hoping that Willard felt the same way. We crossed over a few mountain passes that were clear and wound down through some narrow gorges onto a coastal plain. It was quite a beautiful passage. We then approached a city and followed the signs to Adana. By this time, we had traveled almost three hundred miles and needed gas. We entered Adana after a few miles and stopped at a small service station.

We spoke German with the attendant. He had spent two years in West Berlin digging ditches. He told us that we were about two hours from the Syrian border. He said that the border was closed by this time of day, and that we should spend the night in Adana. He was also kind enough to recommend a decent hotel that happened to accept Master Charge.

We dropped our things into our room there and left to walk around the town. We had decided to go on a diet in the interval between now and when we would see George and Anna again. We had also decided to get some exercise. This plan was thwarted by Willard's knee; it had begun to hurt him again when we started walking around Adana. We limped back to the hotel and went to our room.

"I like the way that you strive so hard to take in the local history and culture, Willard."

"Shit, T, my knee is killing me."

"I know, I'm sorry, man."

I went to my bag and took out my other bottle of Jack Daniel's. We played several different drinking games that night including 99, Wales tails, friends and enemies, and cardinal puff. Most of these games are no good with two people, but we had fun anyway. Willard crashed first; he was still somewhat intolerant of bourbon. I followed soon after, tolerant or not. We both crashed hard.

Having gone to bed quite early, we woke up at the crack of dawn, threw our things in the car, and took off. We stopped for some bread and coffee, but that was it. We followed the road east and got a pretty good look at the Mediterranean. From the map, we could tell that this was its far northeast corner. It didn't look quite as artificially blue as it had in Yugoslavia. We saw it only for a few miles, then entered a small town. There was nothing to see or do there, so we followed the sign to Syria, which by that time was fifty kilometers away. The road turned up into the foothills of another coastal range, and soon we were driving through a narrow cut of solid rock, with one wall rising from the roadway, and the other side embraced unerringly by a handsome stream. There were leaves on the trees, and occasional houses. It was very pretty. The passage opened up into a series of small valleys and smooth hills. It was very green, almost lush, but in a temperate manner. Soon the verdant hills gave way to more semiarid landscape. The signs alerted us that we were approaching the Syrian border.

We approached the Turkish checkpoint. We were greeted at a gate and quite summarily ushered through. They barely talked to us. The road away from the checkpoint wound around some huge boulders. There were several blockhouses with elevated guard towers and turrets. Near the actual border there were five vehicles pulled off to the side of the road. We pulled off behind the last one. There was a group of young men a little older than ourselves standing beside a Mercedes flatbed truck that was about the size of a small American work truck. It had a German tag on it. We greeted them in German and talked with them at length.

"Hello, how are you?"

"We are doing very bad. How about you?"

"We don't know yet. We are going to cross into Syria."

"Good luck. We have been waiting to get across for three days."

Willard and I looked at each other, aghast.

"What's the problem? Do you have a problem with your papers?"

"Our papers are all in order. They are just fucking us around."

There were three of them, and they were all German. They were sort of hippies. They were driving their vehicle to Beirut to sell it. They said that you could make a lot of money doing that. We told them about our plan to sell the VW, and they agreed that we could get 7,500 DM. This was encouraging. They honestly did not know why they were being detained, but they wished us luck. We drove on to the border station.

As we pulled up, we were waved to a parking lot next to a building. We parked and walked in. The man in uniform gave us each a card to be filled out. It was printed in five languages, including English. It wanted personal information and told us to give it to the man with our passports and then to return to our car. We did this and sat patiently in the front seat. After about half an hour, another soldier came out to our car. He did not speak English but read questions to us from one of those phonetic cards. These questions were allegedly in English. They referred to the vehicle.

"Ownership papers, please."

Willard reached into the glove box and searched for something. As he did so, it became obvious that he could not find what he was looking for.

"T, have you seen a leather wallet thing in here?"

"I think I did once, but not for a while. Why?"

"It has the *Tüf.*" The *Tüf* is the German car ownership paper.

"Those bastards in Greece must have lost it when they fixed the car. I can't fucking believe it."

The soldier was waiting patiently.

"What are we going to do? We're really fucked now."

"You better give him something, Willard. Those German guys couldn't get through even with good papers. Isn't there something else? What's this?"

I pulled out a green paper, the top half of which was typed within the confines of a form.

"That's the insurance paper."

"Give it to him."

Willard gave it to the soldier. He looked at it, turned it over, and looked at it more closely.

He read the same sentence.

"Ownership papers, please?"

"This is it. We are Americans and this is what Americans get."

He somehow seemed to understand what Willard had said.

"Serial number?"

Willard pointed to the insurance policy number. The soldier wrote it down.

"Motor number?"

Willard pointed to the expiration date of the policy. The kind fellow wrote it down.

"Make and model?"

Willard was feeling bold. He pointed to the name of the insurance agent. The soldier wrote it down. This farce continued for a few more minutes until all the blanks on the soldier's form were filled in. He then thanked us and walked back to the house. Five minutes later he returned with our passports; visas had been stamped into the back. He said good-bye with a smile and waved us through.

I have never laughed so hard in my life as I did while we pulled away from the border. We waved to the German fellows. They were polite enough to wave back.

"They didn't search us. They didn't question us. They didn't do shit. Thank God that fucker couldn't read or speak English, or German. We could have been anybody or had anything. Can you believe it?"

"I can't believe that you showed him the name of the insurance agent when he asked for the name of the car. Why did you do that, you dumbshit? That was the only thing that was really on there."

"I figured that if we did something right it would ruin the whole thing."

We laughed and laughed. I kept looking at Willard and shaking my head. He kept saying "serial number" in a fucked-up Arabic accent. We slowly calmed down and got into the rhythm of the drive. The road was acceptable. It wound slowly through some scrub hills for quite a few miles, then ascended to a flat, dry plateau. There was nothing to see. We made good time across the desert. I could see a steam train with a short string of cars in the distance running just about parallel to us.

We saw a city in the distance, and our map told us it was Aleppo. On the outskirts I saw a person walking in the distance. As we got closer, she came into view. She was obviously an old woman, stooped and carrying a bundle of sticks. She was covered in black from head to toe, even her face.

"Poor thing. She must have had somebody die recently."

We stared at her as we flew by. Several more people came into view. They, too, were women, and each of them was similarly dressed, shrouded in black, with their faces draped in a fine black mesh.

"Willard. What's going on? This is really weird. This is like the land of the dead."

We soon realized that all the women were dressed in black and covered up. They sometimes had children in tow and usually were carrying something on their backs. I felt an uneasiness grow over me, that old feeling of not belonging, of being in the wrong place at the wrong time. I noticed Willard was driving a little faster.

We still had gas, but we decided to stop at a gas station anyway. A group of young boys ran it. They descended on us and crowded around our open windows. They were speaking to us in about five languages. Willard spoke and they all changed to English.

ROBERT TIBOLT

"We need some gas."

"Of course. Would you like regular or super?"

"Regular is fine."

They filled us up and washed all of our windows. The station was merely a shack with two tired old pumps.

"How far is Aleppo?"

"It is only a few kilometers. It is a big city."

"How far is Hama?"

"I do not know."

They talked and argued for a minute.

"We think it is about two hundred kilometers down that road." It was close to midday. We were still on our diet and weren't especially hungry. We decided to press on and try to make it to Hama before nightfall. Aleppo was a little out of our way.

"We don't have any Syrian money."

"What do you have?"

Willard held out a handful of change from his pocket. It contained an assortment of Greek, German, Turkish, Yugoslav, and Austrian coins. The oldest boy very carefully and knowledgeably picked through the coins and took about a dozen.

"This is enough."

"Are you sure?"

"Yes, thank you."

"Thank you. Good-bye."

We pulled out and started laughing again.

"I figure that cost us about seventy-five cents. This place is going to be cheap."

We pressed on. The afternoon sun was bright but not warm. We got used to seeing the black-clad women on the roadside. We saw very few men. All of the ones we saw were quite old. They wore the same

68

plaid or houndstooth headwear that we had seen on the men talking to George at the Istanbul Hilton. Some of the patterns were red and some black. Most of the men wore very baggy black pants. There were no other fashion statements being made.

We drove through the afternoon and on into dusk. There was a small amount of traffic, mostly work trucks and small transports. As it darkened, the headlights came on and, needless to say, they were all set on high. It was really blinding. We again tried to flash to the oncoming cars and trucks, but again to no avail. So we joined the crowd and kept our high beams on all the time. We approached Hama.

At night it seemed like a tiny strip of a town. We did notice about three hotels on the main drag and saw one that looked decent. I saw the necessary Master Charge sticker on the window, and we stopped.

"*Marhaba.*"

"Hello," Willard said. I looked at Willard standing next to the clerk and realized that he could pass for one of them. He had black hair, a short black beard, and dark eyes; not too tall and that sly, beady-eyed look. I laughed. I didn't even come close. I was fair-haired with blue eyes, six feet, and two twenty.

"We would like to spend the night."

"Of course, sir. Would you please sign the register?"

His English was a hell of a lot better than my Arabic. We were very tired and hungry.

"Where can we eat a good meal at a good price, please?"

"Please, sir, there is a fine restaurant across the street. It is run by my brother. If you would be so kind."

We dropped off our traveling bags, parked the car on the side, and walked to the restaurant. It was quite a small dive but, as usual, the food was spectacular: an assortment of yogurt spreads, flatbread that was warm and tinged with small flecks of carbon, wonderful spicy lamb, and hot soup. We drank mineral water and coke.

"I don't think that they drink alcohol in Arab countries."

"Maybe we can educate them."

"Right."

We finished our meal and left the restaurant. Willard's knee was still hurting, so we just strolled around the main street. Again, there was nothing to see. There were really only a few old stores with virtually no merchandise. There were no people out on the street. We just went to bed.

The drive to Damascus the next day was easy. It only took a few hours. The scenery was drab. It was a sandy, windy place. We didn't stop for anything. We approached the outskirts of the city; we could tell it was a big place. We started to see more people. In addition to the black-clad women, we began to see some young men. They were all in uniform, different kinds of uniforms, from olive-drab fatigues to camouflage to dress military. The other salient feature was that the men walked hand in hand with one another.

"Your friends here seem to have a somewhat different perspective on interaction between and within the sexes."

"This is really fucking weird, T."

Damascus was old. Everything we saw was old, except for a few newer-looking buildings. There were large billboards with relatively crude drawings of President Assad with logos in Arabic. We drove around for a little while then stopped the car, parked, and planned on finding the Hotel Gondola and eating, not necessarily in that order. I asked several people on the street where the Hotel Gondola was and no one knew. They were all very kind, spoke good English, and tried very hard to think of where it might be, but none of them had ever heard of it. We were getting a little discouraged. Then I saw a policeman.

"Excuse me, sir. We are looking for the Hotel Gondola."

"I am sorry?"

"The Hotel Gondola."

He stood and looked blankly back at us.

"Gon-do-la," I said, "it is a kind of boat they use in Venice."

"*Venezia?*"

"Yes."

"Hotel Gondola? I do not know this place."

"Thank you anyway."

Just then there was a loud screeching roar above us, actually two or three. Several jets, military type, were performing acrobatics at a very low altitude over the city. I had built models when I was younger, and I recognized them as MiG-19s. They were an old aircraft and had not been a frontline fighter for the Soviet Union for quite a few years.

"Those are MiGs, Willard."

His eyes followed them as they trailed off toward the horizon.

"No shit."

We looked at each other, wide-eyed and impressed.

"How in the hell are we going to find this fucking place? I guess it's fair to say that it's not on par with the Hilton. Nobody's even heard of it."

"You mean, if it exists at all."

"Don't say that. Let's get something to eat."

We stopped at a bank and exchanged one of our few remaining German traveler's checks for Syrian money. We found a sidewalk cafe and ate lunch al fresco. We had a good view of the city streets. There were soldiers everywhere, holding hands with each other as noted previously. We saw far fewer women. There was a central latrine that was open air, used by both sexes. There were quite a few commercial enterprises, certainly more than we had seen since Turkey. We had a nice lunch, then got up to redouble our search for the famous hotel. I asked at the restaurant, but nobody knew about it. Then I asked the first man that we encountered on the street.

"It is not far from here."

I shook his hand. He actually led us to it. It was only about a half mile away. He was very nice, middle-aged, in a business suit.

"We do not see many Americans here. But we like Americans. It is only the American government that we do not like."

"Oh."

I didn't know what else to say, so I said nothing. Neither did Willard. We turned a corner, and there it was. There was an old, slim sign with the name on it spelled vertically in English letters. We thanked the man very warmly, and he wished us a good visit in Damascus. We walked into the lobby of the hotel. It was a real dive. There were several young men hanging around and behind the desk was an older man.

"We are looking for Abu Adnah."

"I am Abu Adnah, the proprietor of the hotel. How can I help you?"

"We are friends of George, the bicycle racer. He told us to come stay with you."

"You are friends of George. Welcome. Have you seen him lately?"

"Yes. We were with him until only a few days ago."

"Where was that?"

"In Turkey."

"Hmm."

"We would like to stay at the hotel with you for a few days, until George comes."

"Yes, of course. George is coming here?"

"Yes. He is going to meet us here."

"Good. Register here, please."

Willard signed the register and confirmed that they accepted MC. We retrieved the car and parked it out front. We carried in all of our things and were assisted to our room. It was an open cubicle with two beds. The window was half-covered with paper that had some holes in it. There was an iron stove in the middle of the room. Above it was suspended a six-inch sphere with a spigot on the bottom. The smoke-stack loosely passed through the ceiling to the outside. The room was permeated with the smell of oil. The floor was bare linoleum and dirty, and there was no furniture but for the beds. We felt a terribly cold draft from the window.

"Would you show us how the stove works?"

The young man did not speak English, but he got the message. He turned the thumbscrew on the spigot until a slow drip of oil was estab-lished, about one drop every five seconds. Then he took a wooden match and lit the puddle of oil that had formed in the stove. Immediately there was smoke, and after a few minutes there was even a little heat. We went out to the lobby and asked where the bathroom was. We were led down a short hall, and Abu Adnah pointed through a door. In the bathroom there was a hole in the floor that was apparently a toilet. There was a shower head above a tub. By the looks of things, it had not been used in years. I turned on the water to the shower, and a trickle of water equal in magnitude to the flow of the oil through the spigot appeared.

"This is disgusting."

"We have to have a talk with George about this."

We returned to our room and hung up a few things in the closet.

"Let's get out of this rathole."

CHAPTER 10

We left the hotel and began to walk around the city. Our first impression was right. It was old. Buildings were made from stone that looked like it came out of ancient quarries by slave labor. Stone steps were all concave in the middle from the millions of feet that had pounded them through the ages. This contrasted with the almost constant aerial displays of MiG-19s directly above the city. We saw a street vendor selling orange juice and walked over. The oranges looked normal on the outside but were red on the inside. The vendor called them blood oranges. He squeezed two glasses for us. I had never drunk anything so refreshing and tasty in all my life. We paid for the juice with two Greek coins that we figured were worth about seven cents.

It was a busy city. We walked around a commercial area and happened upon a movie theater. We didn't recognize any of the movies playing, but there was a big crowd in line, so we decided to go. In front of us there was a group of four guys about our age. They were joking around with each other. They were obviously locals. Each was dressed in Western-style clothes with leather waistcoats, and three of the four were wearing the same patterned head cloth that most of the male population wore.

"Excuse me, please. What is this movie?"

They all stopped speaking simultaneously.

"Are you American?"

"Yes," I said. "Is this a good movie?"

"It's not as good as an American movie. It is a Saudi movie, and the actress is very famous. But I do not think you have heard of her."

He pointed to a poster.

"No, you're right."

"Are you on holiday?"

"Yes we are. I am Bob and this is Bill."

"We are students at the university. I am Assad. My friends and I are very pleased to meet you."

I could not understand the other names that they rattled off. We shook hands all around.

"Would you like to sit with us?"

"Yes, thank you, very much."

They paid for our tickets. I got the feeling that it was not very expensive. The crowd was quite mixed. Almost all of the young men were in uniform, except for our friends. There were also more Anglo-appearing men in olive-green uniforms scattered throughout the theater. We sat down in the back and ate popcorn.

"See those soldiers?" Assad pointed to the Anglos in green uniforms. "They are all Russians."

It became clear to me: MiG-19s in the sky, Russian soldiers in the theater. I remembered that Syria got its support from the Soviet Union, especially for its military machine, to fight the Israelis. The lights went down and the curtain in front of the screen opened.

"You will enjoy this first movie."

The black-and-white film began, and it showed battle scenes and soldiers.

"This is a movie about the war that we had with Israel."

It showed aerial dogfights between MiG-21s and F-4s. I recognized the American-built Phantom, our mainline fighter-bomber for so many years. One clip showed a surface-to-air missile, a Russian SAM, striking a Phantom and knocking it out of the sky. The crowd went wild. I specifically watched the Russians, but they almost all sat quietly without changing expressions. Clip after clip of similar scenes were shown, with similar crowd responses. I looked at Willard and could tell that he felt like I did—that old feeling came back. I had never seen such a barrage of anti-American propaganda. At least that's how it felt. I had never seen American jets take this kind of abuse. I had always heard of kill ratios in the Second World War, Korea, and Vietnam of multiple enemy aircraft downed for each American aircraft lost. This was emotionally hard to take. Our friends were cheering wildly with each Israeli Phantom and Mirage that blew up or crashed. I felt hollow, scared, and alone.

The short ended and the lights went up. The crowd had been worked into a pretty good frenzy. I wondered if our friends were going to stand up and announce that we were Americans.

"How did you like the film?"

"It was difficult to see all of those American-built jets get shot down. I did not realize that they were part of your enemies' army."

"You must be joking. How do you think Israel survives? It would not last one month without America's support."

"You must hate America."

"We do not hate America. We hate the American government. We do not think that the American people support the Zionists. We think that if they knew the truth about our situation that they would not keep supplying the murderous Jews with weaponry and money to continue their genocide."

The main movie was beginning, mercifully. It was a story about a man and a woman who fell in love and were then separated by war. They each longed feverishly for the other, and much of the movie was spent in reading letters to each other, back and forth. They each had several opportunities to make love with other people, but they refused. Our friends sat uniformly fixated by the plot, and especially by the actress. She was kind of ugly with big tits, a solid butt, and thick legs. They loved her. Willard and I were yawning at each other by halftime. The movie continued on and finally ended. They both died. It was very sad. They never saw each other again. Everybody loved it. There were four subtitles.

We all got up and the crowd seemed much different than it had been before the movie. The Russian soldiers really looked Russian. All of their uniforms were decorated with numerous stars on their epaulets. The local soldiers were dark and mostly small, though there were also some very good-sized fellows. It had definitely become another world in my eyes.

"How did you like the movie?"

"It was too sad." Willard shook his head as he replied.

"How about you, Bob?"

"Nobody ever got laid."

"Pardon me?"

"No sex."

"That is all right. We hardly ever have sex here."

We all laughed.

"We are very passionate people. If we love someone, we will love them forever, no matter what. If you met someone once and fell in love with her, it would not matter if you never saw her again. You would love her, always."

We walked down the main drag. There were six of us. The Syrian guys all crowded around us and bombarded us with conversation. Only Assad spoke good English. The others' English was broken, and Assad mostly translated what they said to us. They all seemed to understand what Willard and I said, though, with a little help again from Assad. They were very friendly guys.

"Maybe we can go back to your hotel."

"We can go there, but it's a dive."

"Pardon me?"

"It's a bad place."

"Oh. We do not care."

"Do you guys ever drink beer?"

"Almost never. We are not allowed to."

"Let's go back to our hotel and drink some beer."

"All right."

We walked in the direction of our hotel and stopped at a corner market next to it. Willard and I bought a case of Syrian beer. We all marched through the "lobby" of the Gondola and to the room. The lazy young men "working" there were lounging about. We got into our room and opened up the beers. Two of the guys had never had a drink. Needless to say, they were shit-faced after half a beer each. They were laughing and giggling and being loud. It was a riot. Assad began to translate what they were laughing about.

"Ali wants to know if you have ever had a woman."

We all laughed.

"Sure, lots of times."

Ali et al. howled with delight.

"How about you guys?"

They looked at each other and mumbled a few words back and forth.

"Ali and I have done it with a whore. She came to our village, and we went out into a shack in a field to do it with her."

"Pretty fuckin' good." I nodded at Willard.

We told them about some routine sexual adventures, and they went apeshit. Unfortunately, one of the rookies had to boot in the shithole down the hall. At least he knew that we didn't have a bathroom in our room. The beer was bad; it was watery with a skunky taste.

"I want to teach you a song."

"What's it about?"

"It is like the movie. It tells about a very great love. Listen: *We oolloo makamah oolloo /*

habei takka in tau bus / la baadi dahab oolooloo."

We sang the song a hundred times. We then taught them a song: Country Joe's classic, the "Gimme an F" song. They learned it pretty well. Assad couldn't understand one thing, though.

"What is this 'fucking?'"

We really howled.

"It is hard to explain."

Willard had gone into his staccato over-pronunciation mode, which he did when he started to get drunk.

"The word itself means to have sex. It is a bad word. But we use it to make whatever we are saying stronger."

We drank about three-quarters of the case. They were hilarious. Assad stood on the bed and screamed, "I am Assad, the lion!" Then they calmed down and became pensive.

"We would like you to meet a friend of ours. He is a Marxist. You will learn much from him."

We went out into the city and walked for about half a mile. We stopped at an old grey building and passed through a wooden door into a small, dark, covered courtyard. It was very old with a fountain in the middle. We knocked on the door of the corner apartment. An older fellow opened the door. He was about thirty, five foot nine, and overweight. He was dark with a dark beard. He spoke in Arabic with Assad and turned around and walked into his place. It was the tiniest of studios wedged in under an oil tank. There was no window. It smelled like the room back at the Gondola. The walls and shelves were covered with military and war artifacts, like twenty millimeter cannon shells, wingtips from jets, shrapnel, other bullets and hand grenades, etc. Abu Saddam was his name.

"So, you are Americans."

"Yes. Nice to meet you." We said our names and shook hands.

"What brings you to Damascus?"

"We are traveling students."

"What are you studying?"

"Premedicine."

"I am happy to meet you, and I am glad that my friends brought you over."

"Where did you get all of this stuff?" I waved my arm around the room.

"Different places. This wing part is from an Israeli Phantom that was shot down not far from here."

"We know how you feel about the American government."

"How do I feel about the American government?" He stared at me.

"You hate it."

He nodded.

"Enough of that. Have you ever been to Syria before?"

"Never. But we sure like it."

"I do not think there is very much to like here for you, but I agree with you. It is a beautiful country. It is an old country. The people are very friendly. We have been at war for many years, though, and it is very hard for us. The Israelis have taken our land and killed many of our people. They are expansionists and are always looking for new territory. What do you know of the situation here in the Middle East?"

"Not very much. Israel is our ally. We believe that their cause is a just one, that they are an island of democracy in a sea of totalitarianism; that they are fighting for their survival in their historical home."

"These things are lies. They occupied their territory illegally and caused the deaths and relocations of many Palestinians. They use American weaponry and technology to protect their illegal claims. How can this be just?"

He spoke English very well. He was very passionate in his beliefs and statements. He did not seem to hold any personal animosity toward us, which was already becoming a recurring theme. I wondered how the average American would feel if the citizens of some other country supplied Mexico with state-of-the-art weaponry to kill Americans. I did not think we would be so charitable. We stayed at Abu Saddam's place for several hours, talking mostly about politics. Our other friends sobered up after sleeping on some pillows in the corner. It became time to leave.

"Assad told us that we would learn a lot by meeting you. He was right. Thank you very much for your hospitality. We hope to see you again."

"Thank you for coming by. We will see each other again."

Our friends walked us back to the Gondola, said good night, and then walked off into the night. We made arrangements to meet them again the next day. We broke out the rest of the beer and had a few. We talked some more about the subjects of the evening. We were quite struck by all that we had learned. I did not feel like going to bed, but Willard was beat. I drank the last beer and went out for a walk in the city.

It was very dark and quiet. I stayed pretty close to the Gondola. I happened to see a young man who was apparently waiting for a bus. I asked him if there was anywhere to go for a beer.

"I know of one place that is probably open. I will take you there."

I had begun to trust people more since I had been in this part of the world. I felt no sense of danger with anyone whom I had yet met. We walked down the mandatory dark alleys and ancient stairways into a smoky bar that was quite reminiscent of the place in Istanbul that the old toothless man had taken us to. It had the same whining music, and apparently the same overweight belly dancer. The crowd was a little livelier. It was actually great fun. I bought the young man some tea. He excused himself after a few minutes and said that he had to get back to the bus stop. He asked me where I was staying. He asked whether I could find my way back. I assured him that I could, and he politely excused himself. I continued to drink a little more and helped close down the place. I walked out afterward and stumbled around the city until I found some familiar landmarks. I think it took me about an hour to walk back, but I finally found the Gondola. I let myself in and crashed.

We were awakened simultaneously by two things. One was the bitter cold and snow that was falling through cracks in the ceiling and windows. The other was my friend from the night before who stopped by to make sure that I made it home all right. I couldn't believe how nice these people were. He started our stove for us as he talked.

"Did you like the bar? I had never been there before."

"Yes, it is a good place. We will have to go back."

Willard was huddled in his bed.

"This is my friend Bill."

Willard stuck his head out from the blankets and chattered a frosty hello through shivering teeth. Finally, the room warmed up as the stove cranked on. The nice young man said he was glad I made it back all right and said that he had to get to work. I never even got his name.

"What was that all about, T?"

"He took me to another belly dancer bar last night, but then he had to leave. I walked home after that."

"You crazy fucker."

"It was a piece of cake. There's no danger out there. This place is safe. I don't think there's one criminal in all of Damascus."

"Right."

We finally got out of bed. I went to take a shower. It was virtually impossible to get wet enough to wash or shampoo, but I guess it was better than nothing. I could see the trail left by our buddies from yesterday. Time to leave the Gondola. We stopped by the desk.

"Have you heard from George?"

"No, George has not come yet," said Abu Adnah.

"You may want to send one of your boys into the bathroom. It's a mess."

We had made a plan to meet our friends at the university about noon. Willard and I prowled around and found a place to have coffee and some food. There was about two inches of snow on the ground, and it was cold as shit. We had some pretty good parkas and boots, so it was no big deal. We walked over to the university area and hung around the student union. Physically, it was terrible. It was not so old, just ratty and weather-beaten. It was a very institutional-appearing facility, like the apartment buildings in Yugoslavia. Our friends came up and shook our hands and hugged us.

"How are you, my friends?"

"We are fine. It was not hard to find your university. Bob went exploring last night and saw some of the finer sights of Damascus."

"Oh, what was that?"

"Some bar with a belly dancer."

"Was it good?"

"Yeah, it was okay."

"I would like to do that myself sometime. We would like you to come out to our village with us. You would honor us by eating a meal. We will also show you the school where we work. Would you be able to come tomorrow?"

"We'd love to."

They had a map that showed their village outside of town.

"Come at nine o'clock."

They had to return to their classes, so Willard and I walked around the campus for a while. There was not much to see. We branched out and walked through the city some more. It was a great city to walk around. We found a big market like the one in Istanbul; this one was called Al-Hamidiyah Souq. It was a good one. We felt like old pros in the haggling department. We didn't buy anything, but we did some very aggressive window shopping. We basically imitated George, handling things in a rough way, looking at something else when the shopkeeper was showing an item, being rude. It earned us some bargaining credibility; we didn't use it but it was nice to have. We stopped and had some food at the marketplace and then found our way back to the Gondola after having the mandatory glass of fresh-squeezed blood orange juice. The regulars were all there.

"Have you heard from George yet?"

"We have heard nothing."

We walked back to our room.

"I wonder if he's going to show."

"It's been less than a week."

"I know, but something doesn't feel right."

"If worse comes to worst, we can always go to Beirut by ourselves."

"Yeah, if we can even get the car through the border. Somehow, I don't think it will be the same at the Lebanese border. I think they're smarter."

We took it easy that night. It had stayed cold through the day. We cranked up the oil stove and got the room pretty warm. We played cards and talked.

"How's your crotch rot?"

"It's getting bad again. How about you?"

"It's starting to itch."

"That's how it starts. You got it."

"You fucker."

That was about the most interesting part of the conversation. We turned in and shivered through the night.

CHAPTER 11

I woke up first. It was freezing. I fired up the stove and scrambled back to bed. After a while it became bearable, and I got up again. It was too cold to shower in this rathole of a hotel. The water wasn't hot and there wasn't enough of it. I think hygiene was part of the problem with the crotch rot. I was sure, though, that nobody else here would notice any lack of hygiene on my part.

"Get up, you slug."

"It's too cold."

"You fucking pussy. Get up. It's after eight."

"Okay."

Willard dragged his dirty, corpulent carcass out of the flea-bitten bed. I had to laugh.

"What's so funny?"

"You look like shit. You couldn't get laid in a whorehouse."

"You should look at yourself, fuckwad. You're the ugliest bear of a human that I've ever seen."

I looked at myself, and he was right. I didn't even know how much I weighed, but it was far more than I had ever weighed. I had long, greasy, ratty hair that came down on the sides to a full beard, but for a bare chin that made it into mutton chops, gnarled and very thick. We both started laughing.

"Talk about ugly Americans."

We got dressed in warm clothes and walked through the lobby.

"Don't tell us. You haven't heard from George."

"I have not."

"I asked you not to tell me." I laughed stupidly.

Willard drove and I got out the map. We drove through the quiet streets and found our way to the road out of town. The city broke up into arid plots with stucco houses. Soon we came to some bleak hills. The road wound up through some rocky crags, snow-covered and rough. It straightened out again and we finished the few miles to their town. We drove into the village. It was a dirty, old, poor town. There were no cars. The only transportation was a single donkey cart. As soon as we drove in, we were surrounded by many people, both adults and children. Moments later, our friends appeared and waded through the crowd to our car.

"Good morning."

"Good morning, my friends."

"Your map was good. It was very easy to find."

"I'm glad. Would you like some tea?"

"Yes, please."

We were brought a few doors down into a shop. We all said, *"Ahlan,"* which is the way of replying hello to more than one person. It was very warm in there; the oil stove was going full blast. They brought out a tray of tea. I ambled about the store. There were about seven different things for sale, all worthless. I smiled at the toothless shopkeeper.

"Assad, would you please tell your friend thank you for the wonderful warm tea? He is very kind."

Assad did so, and the gentleman beamed happily and bowed several times. We didn't say much. It was so comfortable to sit quietly in the warmth and savor the sweet tea.

"Shall we go to our school?"

"Sure."

We walked out and were met by the same waiting crowd. They followed us through the village as we walked to their school.

"In our country, every man must join the army when he turns eighteen. One can avoid this only by performing volunteer service. We have all volunteered to serve as part-time teachers at this school."

We reached the school. It was an old stucco building surrounded on three sides by a six-foot wall. They gave us a tour of the two schoolrooms. Needless to say, they were sparse, with a blackboard, stove, and teacher's and students' desks. We then walked out to the backyard. There was a dirt area and a small basketball court. Assad asked us if we wanted to play basketball. We said sure. A couple of guys grabbed brooms and swept off the snow from the court. They went inside and got a basketball. We watched them play for a bit. They were very uncoordinated; they dribbled like girls using their off hands and shot with a very spastic motion. Then Willard and I got our chance. Willard had played basketball in high school, and I had played quite a bit too. We dribbled, shot, made layups, and threw bounce passes. We looked around and it seemed that the entire town—men and boys—had come out to watch us play. They were standing on the footing of the outside of the wall, hanging shoulder to shoulder. They went wild with every basket, and just about everything else. It was awesome. Willard dribbled behind his back once, and they went bonkers. Our friends were trying to keep up with us on the court. They ran excitedly by our sides, laughing and screaming like children. I took a jump shot from the foul line and made it.

MEET ME IN BEIRUT

It was pandemonium. I looked around and there were hundreds of people going nuts.

We divided into teams, three on three; Willard and I played on opposite sides. We covered each other and played pretty tight D. We both mostly passed off to our buddies, but occasionally would shoot or drive for the hoop. Willard's knee was doing pretty well. He made some great shots, and I did okay myself. The crowd definitely got its money's worth. I don't think that they had ever had this much fun. Neither had we, for that matter. Finally, we had to stop. We got a rousing ovation from the crowd, and we all gave each other high fives and tens too. They loved that. They surrounded us as we left the schoolyard and escorted us to our car. For a moment I knew what it was like to be famous.

We and our friends piled into the car, and we drove over to Assad's house. A few kids ran behind us for part of the way and then peeled off into a walk. We were still laughing when we got there. We climbed out of the car, scattering a group of chickens. Up walked Abu Saddam, the fellow from the other night.

"What a pleasant surprise. How are you doing?"

"Very well, thank you. We are glad that you are able to come here."

Assad excitedly chattered to him, apparently telling him of the events at the school. He laughed wholeheartedly and shook our hands again.

Abu Saddam pointed to the flock of chickens.

"Which one do you want?"

"What do you mean?"

"Tell us which chicken you want to eat."

"It doesn't matter."

"Please tell us which chicken you want to eat."

I shrugged my shoulders and pointed to a white one. They quickly cornered it, grabbed it by its wings, and slit its throat with a pocketknife.

They let it go. It ran around, scattering blood everywhere until it collapsed. Willard and I looked at each other quizzically. It was then that I saw a woman peeking at us from around the corner. When I turned to look at her, she disappeared. For the rest of the day, I saw only brief glimpses of females, shrouded from head to toe, with only their eyes exposed.

"Come."

We followed them to a room. The house was made of a string of rooms connected by common walls, but each one with its own door to the outside, and no inside hallway. It was stucco, with exposed round log beams. Assad swept aside the cloth hanging in the doorway. We stooped to enter. Inside was a warm, comfortable room. It was covered with carpets on the floor, with only a single low table. The walls were also covered with carpets, and there were many large pillows on the floor. We pulled up a pillow and sat around the table.

CHAPTER 12

I hope that you are both hungry."

"I'm starving. You guys wore me out on the basketball court."

"You are both so good at basketball. I wish we could play so well."

"We had a good game. You all had some good plays."

The seven of us had settled around the table. I guess the parents weren't invited. I had seen an older man for a minute, but he did not appear again.

"Do you like to hunt? We will go hunting after our meal."

Willard had hunted all of his life. I had been hunting several times, every time with Willard, and had yet to kill anything.

"Sure."

"Good."

"Where is the bathroom?"

"Do you wish to bathe?"

"No, I must urinate."

"Oh. There is a house in the back."

Willard excused himself and left.

"That reminds me. I have not seen any toilet paper anywhere."

"What is toilet paper?"

"You use it to wipe yourself after taking a shit."

"A shit?"

"Yes, you know . . ." I grunted and pointed to my ass.

"Oh. We wipe with water. You use paper?"

"Yes. Everyone in America uses paper."

Assad discussed this point in earnest with the other guys.

"We do not think that you can get yourself entirely clean with paper."

"Maybe you are right."

"We use our left hand to wash ourselves afterward." He held his hand out to show me which one he meant. "That is why we shake hands with the other."

"I'll have to try using just the water. How do you get dry?"

"We do not get dry."

"Hmm."

"Maybe it would be best to use both water and paper. I think this would work, to use both of our methods."

"Yes, I think you're right."

Willard returned. I whispered to him.

"I hope you didn't wipe your ass with your right hand."

"There wasn't any toilet paper."

Just then there was a knock at the door and Abu Saddam stood and walked over. Bowl after bowl of steaming food was handed through the doorway into his waiting hands; we passed them bucket brigade-style until they just about filled the table. Hot fresh bread was used as plates, and we dug into a wonderful meal of chicken, rice, yogurts, peppers, and other vegetable condiments. Even Willard and I could not eat it all.

We lounged around for a few minutes afterward. Assad made me sing the song he had taught us. Abu Saddam really liked that. We talked about general stuff—no more politics. I could tell that everyone was very comfortable. Some hot tea was handed through the portal, and we relaxed even more. It was very cozy.

"Let us hunt."

We all got up and put on our jackets. We tried to follow the others out, but they insisted that we go first. Assad ran into the house and returned with a double-barrel shotgun. He had a pocketful of shells.

"It is Russian," he said as he handed it to me. I looked it over and passed it to Willard. He examined it more knowledgeably and gave it back to Assad.

"It's a piece of shit," he muttered.

We tramped off single file into a howling wind that had blown up during lunch. It was not snowing, but it was bitterly cold. Snow was blowing around, powdery and crisp. The trail led into some fields surrounded by bare trees and stone walls. Willard turned to me and yelled into the wind.

"This looks like bird heaven. We should see lots of action."

We walked for quite a while. We saw nothing. There were no birds, no tracks in the snow, no nothing. We stopped and milled around in a circle. Willard turned to me again.

"They must've killed everything that has ever lived here. There should be all kinds of stuff around here."

Assad gave the shotgun to Willard. He moved to the front of the line and led us through the edge of a thicket. As we approached it, there was a rush of two little tweety birds toward us and then over our heads. Willard got off a shot, but he missed.

"Damn."

Assad gave him two shells and he reloaded. Willard turned around and gave the gun to me, pointing to a spot near the trigger guard.

"This is the safety. Try not to kill anybody."

I took the gun and led us through the brush into another clearing. A single bird flushed from the grass and began to turn downwind in a tight bank. I had only a fraction of a second to shoot, so I let her rip with both barrels. He never had a chance. Half the guys crowded around me, slapping me on the back, and the others ran over to bring me my prize.

"Fine shot, my friend."

"Whaddya think, Willard?"

"That was a great shot, T. I can't believe you made it. Into the wind and everything. Unbelievable."

Two of the fellows walked up cradling the poor, hammered, sparrowlike creature in the cupped palms of their hands, offering it to the great white hunter. I picked it up. After a few seconds of disdainful inspection, I tossed it aside. You should have seen the look of horror on their faces. They ran over to it and one of them grabbed it, held it covetously, and then stashed it in his pocket. Willard and I looked at each other.

"Oh boy."

We trooped back through the broken fields and didn't see one more sign of life. I kept looking for the little shed where Assad and his buddy had gotten laid, but I never saw it. We made it back to the house and warmed ourselves in the dining room with hot tea.

We talked a little more. Abu Saddam had heard of George. He wanted to meet him when he came to Damascus. I wasn't quite sure that he would get the chance.

"We have already been here for over a week longer than George said it would be. I don't know how much longer we can stay. We both must be getting back to our schools."

"Could you go to Beirut? Perhaps George is waiting for you there."

"He swore he would come for us here. If he doesn't come here, there is no reason to expect that he would even be in Beirut."

MEET ME IN BEIRUT

"I do not know what to say. I am sure that he would be here with you if he could."

"Yeah, but why hasn't he called? He's the one who told us about the Hotel Gondola. He must know the number. I don't think that he's going to show."

Willard and I both knew that ultimately, we had no choice. Our only way back to Germany was through Beirut. We sure as hell weren't going to drive all the way back. Without any real ownership papers, we probably wouldn't even make it out of Syria. At least we had the option of selling the car if we went to Beirut. There was also a chance of a ferry that could take us and the car back to Italy if we couldn't sell it.

"I wonder where the fucker is."

"We hope that it all works out for you. We have been very lucky to have met you."

"We are the ones who are lucky. You have been so friendly and kind. We will never forget any of this."

"Will you write us when you get back to America? We have met a few other foreigners who have written us. It is enjoyable to receive letters."

"You bet. Give us your address."

It was getting late in the day. We exchanged addresses.

"We have to leave now. Thank you again for the wonderful day. You are good friends. We may be leaving Damascus soon, so we wish you the best."

We hugged all around. They kissed us. I even held hands with one of them on the way out of the room. They walked us to the car. Only a few children ran after us on the way out of town.

We drove slowly back to the Gondola and parked it in the street. We walked into the lobby. Abu Adnah was there, as usual. I didn't ask him if he had heard from George, but I guess my look did.

"I have not heard from George."

"We figured as much."

We walked back to our room. We broke out the last bottle of scotch and began to hammer on it. Soon the room wasn't so cold, and we weren't so depressed.

"Let's go to Beirut tomorrow."

"I agree. We're out of here."

We went to bed. The next morning, we woke up to a hard freeze. I got the stove going. Willard finally got out of bed.

"I thought you wanted to go to Beirut."

"Let's give him a couple more days."

"What for?"

"He said he was going to come, and I believe him. If we leave now, we might miss him."

"So what. We have his number in Beirut. We'll call when we get there."

"Let's just give him three more days. That will make it three weeks in Damascus."

"Whatever you say, Willard."

We had literally walked every part of Damascus. We knew the city inside and out. We got our warm clothes on again and walked outside. We were walking in the direction of one of our breakfast spots. On the way was a very fancy building that we had passed many times. Today there was a fairly large crowd outside the front door. Not as many people were there as had been watching us play basketball, but almost. We joined the crowd and hung around. After a few minutes there was a buzz in the crowd, and we looked to the front door. I could see over everybody's head. I gave Willard an elbow jab to the ribs.

"Look! It's Arafat."

It really was him. He was walking out the front door. He was surrounded by four large Arab types in dark suits. He had on his typical headgear. The crowd went nuts. We clapped too. He went down the walkway right in front of us. I could have touched him. There were three black Cadillac limousines parked out front. His entourage began to fill them up. I had a good view of him the whole time. He got into the middle limo, then climbed straight out the other side. His three body-guards had left him and gotten into a tiny green Fiat, one of those little boxlike 124s. He walked around to the front passenger door and climbed in. The limos all peeled out down one street. The Fiat pulled out from behind them and veered off down another street. This all happened in a flash, and they were gone.

"Wow! Did you see that, Willard? Those guys are slick."

I looked around the crowd. Everyone was still excited and jabbering. I looked across the street and saw a man taking pictures of the crowd. He had a telephoto lens on a 35 mm camera. It looked like he was taking a picture of Willard and me at one point. He panned the crowd once more, then climbed into a Mercedes and took off. He was gone before I could get Willard's attention.

"Some guy just took your picture."

"What are you talking about?"

"Some fucking guy just took our picture, along with the rest of the crowd."

"What for?"

"I don't know."

"Let's go eat."

"Okay."

We hung around Damascus for a couple more days. We had our blood orange juice, retraced our paths around the city again until there wasn't any place that we hadn't been, and heard again and again that George hadn't come.

"We have to go, Willard. There's no reason to wait anymore. He's not coming. Let's get out of here. Let's go to Beirut."

"You're right. Let's go tomorrow."

Our last night in the Gondola was routine. It was cold as shit again when we woke up. It had snowed a little bit. We dressed and went to the lobby. We hadn't showered at all for the last week. Abu Adnah greeted us.

"I am sorry that our friend never showed up."

"Did you know that he wasn't going to come, Abu Adnah?"

"No, I didn't know. I was surprised that he might be coming, though. I haven't seen George in years. He is not a man that you can track."

Willard and I looked at each other, and he paid off the tab with MC. It was pretty cheap. To paraphrase the old saying, you pay for what you get. We loaded up our car. I waved off the lazy boys who tried to get up to help us with our bags. We climbed in the Bondomobile and left the Gondola forever. Willard had filled up the tank the day before. We stopped for one last glass of blood orange juice. This one was on the house; we were his best customers. He pointed us in the direction of the road to Beirut. It would not be long now.

We drove out of town on a cold windy day. On the map it didn't look like more than one hundred kilometers to Beirut. The road was a busy highway by local standards. There were many trucks. The road-way was clear. We were driving up to some pretty rugged hills covered by increasing amounts of scattered snow. It was nasty out. We soon reached the border. It would be our last moment of truth. The Syrian checkpoint was a large brown building with a big parking lot. It was filled mostly with trucks, and there was a fair amount of activity by the border personnel. We drove right up to a lane that had only one car ahead of us. The border guard asked us for our passports and checked our visas. He looked in at us and just eyeballed our things in back through the window. He circled us once and then had us drive over to the side. We both got out. He walked into the building and came back with our passports. He said something in Arabic and waved us through. We drove on quite slowly through a hilly pass, wondering what lay ahead for us at the Lebanese side. The road ran for a few miles before we saw the signs for the border.

We passed the summit and had started to go down a little. We finally got around a big hill and were able to look into the distance. It was unbelievable. Below us lay as lush and green a valley as I had ever seen: Al-Biqa. It was crisscrossed by lines of division between agricultural fields of every hue from green to gold. There was a river in the middle of the valley and irrigation ditches dissecting the fields. Beyond it lay a snow-covered string of mountains running north to south. On the map, the range of hills that we were leaving was the Anti-Lebanon range, and the one before us was the Lebanon range.

We saw the border station. We looked at each other and got into a line of cars. They were letting most people through without searches or any real delay. Then we pulled up to the guard. He had on a long white leather coat and was armed with a handgun on a belt. He greeted us in German.

"Papieren, bitte."

"We're Americans. Here are our passports." Willard gave him both mine and his own.

He looked them over as he walked around our car.

"What have you been doing in Syria?"

"We have been on holiday, actually waiting to meet a friend who never showed up."

"Hmm. What are you doing in Lebanon?"

"The same really. We are looking for some warmer weather."

"It has been very cold. Do you have papers for your car?"

"I'll show you what we have. This is what they gave me when I bought the car."

Willard gave him the green insurance policy. Unfortunately, he could read it.

"This is insurance paper."

"I know."

"You have nothing else?"

"No. I never did."

I looked at Willard out of the corner of my eye and could tell he was doing the same to me.

"This will do." He walked over to the station.

He returned to the car.

"Please step out."

Our feelings of joy were somewhat subdued.

"What do you have in your car?"

"Not much, really. Clothes, some cigarettes, half a bottle of whiskey, some coats that we bought in Turkey, that's all."

"Would you open the back?"

"Sure."

Willard did it. The guard lightly poked around the back. He opened up my traveling bag and sifted through it for a few seconds, then zipped it closed. He then opened up one of the garment bags and slowly felt the suede with his fingers.

"Very nice. How much?"

Willard looked in and saw it was mine.

"Two hundred dollars."

"That is a very good price."

We looked at each other and smiled.

"We know."

"Anything else back here?"

"No."

He closed the hatchback, handed us our passports with new visas stamped in the back, and shook our hands.

"Have a wonderful time in Lebanon."

"Thank you very much." We climbed in and didn't let out any yelling or laughing until we had gone about fifty yards.

"We did it again. I can't believe it. Let's go."

We were rollin'. Willard got on the little car, and we wound our way to the valley floor in no time. Down came the windows. The air was almost warm again and smelled like grass. The sun was shining. It was beautiful.

"I think George may have been right. This place is beautiful."

"That fucker. I'm going to chew his ass when I see him."

"If you see him."

"Yeah."

We scooted along the valley floor. It was lush and green with orchards and fields just full of life. We decided to wait until Beirut to eat. The road quickly began its ascent into Mount Lebanon. We started seeing some snow again. There was at least three feet of new snow at the summit. There were increasing numbers of cars pulled off to the side. Traffic had slowed way down though the roadway was clear. The sun was shining without a cloud in the sky. It would have been a good day for skiing. We discovered that the people had pulled off to go sledding. There were kids everywhere sliding down on everything from cardboard to fancy American sleds. We stopped and got out near the summit. We climbed through the snow to what looked like a vantage point to the west. It was stunning. Beyond lay a big city right next to the blue of the Mediterranean. The scene kind of reminded me of looking at Lake Tahoe from way above it, with the snow and the bright blue water.

"Let's go."

"This is unbelievable."

"It really is."

We drove as fast as we could, within reason. The air got very warm as we descended. The windows came down again. Feeling that warm, moist air blasting through the car as we drove was so nice. We had been cold for a long time. The road led us into Beirut. It was a remarkable city. The approach from the east led us by some fabulous homes. They looked more like embassies or something. It was almost all very modern and beautiful, as clean and nice as anything we had seen since Austria.

"Let's drive all the way down to the water before we stop."

"You got it."

We kept driving and got nearer to the center of the city. We started to see high-rise buildings and offices and hotels, everything new and lovely. We finally reached the road that ran along the sea. We followed it until we came upon a medium-sized high-rise called the Phoenicia. We pulled in.

"I'm going to call that fucking George."

We both walked into the lobby. A nice man at the desk greeted us.

"May I help you?"

"May we use your phone?" Willard was digging through his address book.

"Yes, of course."

He directed us to some house phones on the side of the lobby.

"Give me the number and I will dial it for you."

"Thanks."

Willard got on the phone.

"Hello, is George there?" He listened, then his eyes lit up. "He's there! That son of a bitch!"

"George? You motherfucker! This is Bill and Bob. Where the fuck have you been? We waited for you for three weeks in Damascus. You son of a bitch!"

Willard was smiling at me while he gave George a bad time. He listened and nodded his head, looking at me with a big smile the whole time.

"Let me talk to him," I demanded.

Willard held up his hand.

"Bill is really pissed at you, George. He says he wants to kick your fucking ass." Willard was really smiling now.

"All right, George. We'll see you at twelve-thirty at the White House Apartments. We'll be there. If you're not there, I'm going to tell Bill to tear you a new asshole."

"Never mind. You better be there. All right. Bye."

"What did he say?"

"A bunch of bullshit. But he's there. He wants us to take a cab over to his place, but he'll only be there until twelve-thirty."

"Why do we have to take a cab?"

"He said it's too hard to find."

It was ten now.

"Let's eat."

The man at the desk had returned to the lobby after going outside and looking over our car.

"Is there a good restaurant nearby?"

"Yes, right next door there is a good restaurant for lunch if you like British food. Pardon me, but would you possibly be interested in selling your car?"

"Yes, we are interested in selling it. How much do you think it's worth?"

"How much do you want for it?"

"Two thousand dollars."

"I could pay fifteen hundred. Do you have papers?"

"We have this." Willard showed him the insurance paper.

"This is good. Do you wish to sell your car to me?"

"Maybe not right now. We have to meet a friend first. I will check back with you if you want."

"Here is my card."

"Thank you. Thank you very much. Good-bye."

We walked around the corner into a dark, British-style pub. We ordered some Guinness and sandwiches.

"This is really going to be something."

"You're not shittin'. I can't believe you already had an offer on the car."

"I bought it for thirteen hundred dollars. I can't believe it."

We ate our sandwiches and drank a few beers. I beat Willard at darts. After about an hour, we went out into the sun and walked around the sidewalk. It was nice, definitely high-class tourist action. The Phoenicia was one of many big condos and hotels in this area. It was immaculate. There were boutiques, restaurants, hotels, everything. I had never seen so many pinball arcades in all my life. There were two on every block with all the best, newest games. There were lots of nice cars. I could see why George was bringing his car here. There were lots of other pimpmobiles. They must have really liked that look. All the cabs were Mercedes 180s, old but nice. We definitely were not disappointed.

It was almost eleven-thirty. We were going to go to a bank to exchange some money, but we ran into a guy on the sidewalk in a little booth. He was a money changer. He had all the rates listed on the stand. We gave him DM and he gave us Lebanese pounds. We trusted the guy. We flagged down a cab. We got in. The driver turned around and said something in Arabic.

"Do you speak English?"

"No."

"Deutsch?"

MEET ME IN BEIRUT

"No."

"We want to go to the White House Apartments."

"Vite Hou Apartment?"

"White House Apartments. W-h-i-t-e H-o-u-s-e A-p-a-r-t-m-e-n-t-s."

"Vite Hou Apartment. Vite Hou Apartment. Okay. Okay." He slowly nodded his head as he turned around to drive.

"I wonder if this fucker knows where this place is."

"We'll see."

He drove for quite a while. It was a beautiful day for a drive. We had the windows down and were really relaxed. After about twenty minutes, he pulled in front of a store in a retail district. The sign said West House. It was a dress shop.

"No. No. No. White House. White House Apartments. Apartments. Big. White House."

The poor old guy was really confused. He mumbled to himself and took off, this time faster. He was a little agitated. So were we. It was almost twelve-thirty.

"If the old fart makes us miss George, I'm going to kill him."

He drove for another fifteen minutes and pulled to a stop again. We couldn't tell where we were, except that it wasn't anything like the White House Apartments. We were pissed.

"Let's go."

We got out and started to rag at him.

"You got us lost twice, you wasted all our time, you probably made us miss meeting our friend that we've been trying to meet for three weeks. Fuck you."

We started to walk away. The old man walked as fast as he could to head us off. He was pissed. He kept sticking out his hand like he wanted money, yelling the whole time. We were yelling back at him and tried to walk away. He got in front of us and stopped us each time. We wanted to find another cab before we missed George. Just then the guy started reaching slowly under his sport coat lapel, palm to his chest, like he was going for a gun or a knife. I knew what to do. I kept looking at the man and didn't change my tone of voice.

"On three Willard. One. Two. Three."

We both dashed down the street at once, even surprising ourselves with our action. He didn't have a gun; at least he didn't shoot us. He tried to run after us but that only lasted about twenty feet—then he stopped in a huffing rage. We kept looking back until we had lost him. We cut down a few side streets. We started walking and suddenly saw another cab. We both started yelling and waving, and the guy stopped for us. We climbed in and barked out "White House Apartments" between gasps of breathlessness.

"Sure thing."

We got there in about ten minutes.

CHAPTER 13

We had driven down what was apparently one of the main drags of Beirut, a street in Al Hamra. It was a busy commercial district loaded with everything that a real city person could want. We drove down to the end of Hamra, then the cabbie slowed down and started looking for some cross street that the White House was on. He was crawling along when Willard spotted it.

"There it is—White House Apartments!"

We were both slaphappy. Several weeks' worth of frustration was about to come to an end. It was hard to believe that we were really going to hook up with George again.

"Holy shit, Willard, look!"

I was pointing to a cab that was inching around the perimeter of the block that the White House was on. It was the guy that we had ditched.

"Can you believe that the son of a bitch finally found the fucking place? I can't believe it. What do you want to do?"

"I don't know. Let's get out here—stop the car!"

Our cabbie heard us and stopped. We were across a small open lot from the White House, on a street at the opening of an alley. We paid the man and got out. We walked toward the White House, shielded by another building from the front of the apartments where the other cabbie had now stopped. We sneaked up to the edge of the building and peered around the corner like spies, trying to see what the guy would do. He was just sitting there.

"Let's wait a few minutes. He'll probably leave."

"Yeah, but it's already one and I damn sure don't want to miss George. Let's just walk over there."

We did some more sneaking around and peeking from around corners, then we just walked out into the open and crossed the open lot. As we got closer, the cabbie saw us and started to raise hell. We kept on walking right past him into the lobby of the White House. He followed us in. Two big Arab guys came across the lobby toward us and were immediately inundated with the other guy's story. They acted pretty reasonable and tried to calm the guy down. Just then, George walked in.

"Goddam, George, are we glad to see you. This fucker is giving us a really bad time."

"What is the problem?"

We told him our side of the story at the same time that the other guy told his. George did an admirable job of listening to both of us raving in two different languages. I think he got the picture.

"Pay the man."

"What? He fucked us royal. He got lost, then wouldn't admit that he didn't know where the place was, then made like he was going to fucking shoot us. He almost made us miss getting together with you. Fuck him."

"Pay him. Give him five pounds. Just pay him. Trust me."

We had heard George say those words before. We glared at the cabbie as Willard dug out a fiver and slapped it into his hand.

"Now shake hands."

"George!"

"Do it!"

We did it. The guy left. George stood there shaking his head. He was pretty disgusted.

"Hi, George."

"I cannot believe you two. I leave you alone for three weeks and you almost get killed."

"We could have been killed for all you would have known, George."

"I am sorry about Damascus."

Now it was our turn to glare.

"Where in the fuck were you? We stayed in that rathole of a hotel, if you can call it that, for three weeks. I guarantee you wouldn't have stayed there for one night. We froze our asses off, we were filthy; it sucked."

"I have stayed there many times in the past. I am very sorry for not meeting you there. I was delayed in Cyprus, then I was unable to enter Syria."

"Why didn't you just drive up the road to Damascus from here? It's only a couple of hours. We drove it today. And we don't even have any papers."

"What do you mean?"

"Oh, nothing. Why didn't you call?"

"I could not call. It was impossible. We will talk about it later. I want you to meet a friend of mine."

One of the big Arab guys had left. The one who remained was good-sized, about six two, two thirty-five. He walked with a limp. It was hard to tell his age, but he was no more than thirty. He looked a little dopey, but nice. He had on a real shiny-looking vest, with black pants and sort of string tie.

"This is Abu Sultan. He is my friend, bodyguard, valet, everything. These are my American friends Bob and Bill."

I was glad to see by the introduction that George still had our names confused. We shook hands.

"I am very glad to meet you. I am sorry but I do not think we can provide you with any better entertainment than you just provided for yourselves. But we will try."

We all laughed.

"Anna and her mother are shopping. They will be thrilled to see you. Come. I will show you where you will be staying."

We followed them down the hall into a first-floor corner apartment. Abu Sultan had some keys and opened the door. It was empty.

"This is nice, George. Where's the furniture?"

"We will get that today."

Willard and I looked at each other somewhat askance.

"Come on. We have much to do. Where did you leave your car?"

"Over by the Phoenicia, next to the beach."

"We know where that is. Let's go get it right now."

We all walked out and around the back. There was the pimpmobile, none the worse for wear. We climbed in. George was his usual crazy self. It finally all seemed worth it.

"So what happened, George?"

"It is a long story."

"I'm sure."

"I am Iraqi. I cannot enter Syria."

"Now's a great time to tell us."

"I had thought that I would be able to get in from Cyprus, but I was wrong."

"George!"

"This is true."

"We waited in that disgusting Gondola for three fucking weeks. Every day, twice a day, we would ask Abu Adnah if you had shown up. It was very depressing."

"Did you have any fun?"

"Yeah, we met some guys, and we had a good time."

"Well then, what is the problem?"

"It's no big deal, but it was not very nice, George. We were pissed."

"I am very, very sorry. Believe me, if I could have done anything about it, I would have."

"Why didn't you call?"

"I could not."

"Why?" I was very anxious to hear this one.

"I was not at liberty to divulge my location."

"What?"

"I could not let anyone know that I was in the area."

"Oh shit."

"Remember how I told you that I helped my people, and you asked me who my people were?"

"Yeah. You said they were the Palestinians, the Armenians, and the Iraqis."

"That is correct. I am in the PLO."

I sat there, almost stunned. I didn't know why; I didn't even really know what the PLO was. It was just kind of a shock. He reached into his coat pocket and pulled out a picture. It showed him in the same kind of headgear that Arafat wore. He was holding a machine gun and was in some phony war pose. I couldn't believe it.

"You're in the PLO?"

"Yes, and so are my friends like Abu Sultan. He is a soldier. We are dedicated to our cause . . . he was injured in a commando raid into Israel."

"So what does all this mean? Are we prisoners or something?" I laughed.

"Do not be foolish. I would like you to learn about the PLO while you are here. As I told you, you receive a very false version of the truth in America. All of your information is controlled by the Jews. This is well known. But enough of this. I really wanted you to come here to have fun. And I will make sure that you do."

We were getting close to where our car was parked.

"A guy offered us fifteen hundred dollars for the car, George. What do you think?"

"We can do better. First, though, we have to get the body fixed and painted. I have a friend. Why don't we just drive it over there right now and drop it off. He will fix it and I will pay for it. Then you can pay me back when we sell the car."

I looked at Willard. He said okay. Willard and I got out and walked over to his car.

"Follow me," George shouted. We fired up the Bondomobile and tried to stay close to George. He headed into a part of town that we had not yet seen. It was more like the industrial area with lots of shops, warehouses, and trucks. George drove down several alleys and stopped at a real shaky-looking place. It was an old garage with broken windows and no sign. There were some of the sleaziest looking dudes I had ever seen just hanging around. George stopped and got out. He was greeted very warmly by a man who came out of the garage. They talked for a few minutes and then George asked for the keys. Willard reached into his pocket.

"Ah, what the fuck," he said.

I didn't have much to add.

"What did you say about papers?"

"We lost the German ownership papers. Actually, they got lost in Greece when they fixed the car after the second accident."

George got a real funny look on his face.

"Never mind. Do you have any papers?"

Willard got out the green insurance paper and gave it to George. George looked at it and gave it to his body man. He looked it over and took it with him into the shop. Another man came out holding it and rattled something at George.

"He says it will work. We can sell the car with it."

"How much is the car worth?"

"Maybe three thousand dollars."

"Great. What do we do now?"

"Leave it with my friend. He will make it beautiful. It will be ready in a week."

"Whatever you say, George."

"Let's go."

We emptied out our things from our car and put everything in George's trunk. George very carefully moved our garment bags for us, and we climbed in.

"Did you hang up your leather coats while you were in Syria, or did you leave them in the car?"

I looked at Willard.

"We brought them in and hung them up. Don't worry, George, we took good care of them."

"I know you did. Who's hungry?"

"You know we are, George."

"We will get the ladies and go out for a special meal. What do you want to eat? Name it."

"We don't care, George."

"Come on, what do you want?"

"How about fish. We haven't eaten any fish since Yugoslavia."

"Fish, then."

"So what have you been doing, George? How have you spent the last three weeks?"

"No fun. Mostly meetings."

"What kind of meetings?"

"It is hard to explain right now. I will explain everything as soon as I can. Tell me, what did you do in Damascus?"

"We saw Arafat."

George almost got in a wreck. He turned his head around so fast that his body turned, too, and his hands slipped off the steering wheel.

"Where did you see him?"

"In Damascus, of course."

"What was he doing?"

"He was coming out of a nightclub. It was during the day. It was really neat. There were three limos out front. A bunch of people climbed into them, and Arafat got into a tiny Fiat with three big dudes and went another direction."

"Yes, I have seen him do that before. What else did you see?"

"Like what?"

"Did you see anything else?"

"In Damascus?"

"Were you seen there?"

"Where?"

"When you saw Arafat."

"Maybe. I saw some guy taking pictures. Why?"

"Sometimes they have surveillance of such events. It is nothing . . . what else did you do?"

"We walked over every square inch of that city. We know that city inside out."

"Yes, I think you must."

"We saw some movie about the Arab-Israeli war with a bunch of US-made jets getting shot down. We saw a bunch of Russians and Russian aircraft. We went hunting with our Syrian friends. We played basketball in front of a whole town, and we were heroes! We ate like kings and drank blood orange juice every day. That's about it."

"Not a bad three weeks. Was I right? Did you have a good time?"

"We did, George. No thanks to you." I smiled when I said that.

"I knew you would," he smiled back.

We had arrived back at the White House. We all grabbed something to carry. George carried our coats in their garment bags again and led us down the hall to our apartment. Willard and I were utterly surprised to see that there was a pretty good assortment of furniture in it now. There were two beds in the bedroom, a couch and a chair in the living room, cookware and plates and utensils in the kitchen, towels in the bathroom, and the electricity had been turned on.

"You are all set, my friends. What do you think?"

"This is great, George. This is really great. You don't waste time, do you?"

"Not for something that is important. What would you like to do now?"

"Take a shower, and then eat."

"Good. Come up to 606 when you are ready. We will be waiting for you. One other thing. There is a market right down on the corner. You can charge anything you want there. They have beer and food. I will see you, my friends."

George and Abu Sultan walked out.

"What do you think, Willard?"

"I think we're sitting pretty. This is going to be fun."

"You shower first, and I'll go to the store and get some stuff."

"Okay."

I walked out of the front door. The air was warm and moist; dusk had settled and muffled the clamor of the city. Only in the distance could horns and sirens and cars be heard. There were only a few people out walking. It was relaxing in a subtropical way. There were palm trees and lush shrubs. I reached the little store and walked in. The shopkeeper greeted me in Arabic.

"*Ahlan*," I replied, "I am staying at the White House Apartments for a few weeks and would like to pick up some things."

"Welcome. I would be happy to help in any way that I can. What do you care for?"

"First, I must tell you that I am a friend of George in room 606 of the White House Apartments, and he told me that I might be able to run a tab."

"You are a friend of George! You are especially welcome. You would like to place some items on his account?"

"Yes, please."

"Very well. What would you like?"

"For now, some beer would be good. What kind do you have?"

"We have many kinds. German, Dutch, Lebanese."

"How is the Lebanese beer?"

"Quite good. Would you like to try it?"

"Yes, please. Make it a case."

"How many is that?"

"Twenty-four bottles."

"Very good. What else?"

I couldn't think of anything else right then.

"That should do it for now."

He wrote it up, I signed for it, and he put it all into a box. I began my walk home. I saw from the corner of my eye a young man in Arabic headgear. He looked like he was on sentry duty. He walked back and forth in front of a building next to the White House. He was armed with a machine gun. I had to walk in front of him to get home. He watched me very closely and did not return my smile. I was glad to walk into our apartment building. I walked through the lobby and into our apartment. Willard was basking on one of the beds like a lizard on a stone, sprinkling some baby powder on his crotch.

"Just in time. The shower is great. You got some beer?"

"Nothing but the best. Lebanese beer."

"I hope it's better than that Syrian swill."

I showered and dressed. It felt good.

"This stuff isn't bad. Let's have one or two and go find George."

We sat out on a little veranda that we had. It overlooked the alley between us and the building where I had seen the armed man.

"I saw this guy with a machine gun."

"A soldier?"

"I don't think so. He didn't have a uniform. There he is."

"Yeah, no shit. I wonder who the fuck he is. I hope he's friendly."

"Don't be so sure. He didn't act too friendly."

We finished our beers and Willard got dressed. We put on our nicest clothes, took the elevator up to George's place, and rang the bell. Anna answered the door.

"Bob and Bill. I am so glad to see you. I cannot tell you how wonderful it is to see you." She hugged us both.

"You're not half as glad as we are. You look great, Anna. How's your mother?"

"She is fine. Please come in."

George had a nice place. It was furnished with very nice things and had a veranda that looked out over the end of Hamra. It looked past the building with the guard. Anna's mother came in, and we all hugged each other.

"Where's George?"

"Not far away," he answered from the kitchen.

"Hey George, who is the guy with the machine gun out in front of that building?"

"He is a soldier in the PLO."

"What's he doing there?"

"He is standing guard in front of the PLO Research Center. It is in that building."

"Research Center? What do they do research on?"

"It is like a library, with books and magazines in many different languages to assist people in study of Palestinian culture."

"Oh. Why do they need a guard with a machine gun?"

"There is always chance for trouble. Some people think that the Israelis might attack it."

"Why would they attack a library?"

"It is hard to say. They are dangerous and devious. Who is hungry?"

Anna and her mother looked at us and laughed. We had to laugh too. We were pretty hungry. We all walked downstairs. Abu Sultan was waiting for us.

"Good evening, my friends. How are you?"

"We're great. How are you, Abu Sultan?"

"I am good. I may be even hungrier than you two. I have heard of your appetites."

"Where can we walk that has good fish for our friends?"

"I know the place for us. We can pick out fresh fish that they will cook for us. It is a lovely night for a walk."

We struck out down Hamra, first walking by the Research Center building. The guard wasn't there now.

"Where's your buddy, George?"

"Don't worry, he is not far away. There are always at least three soldiers on patrol at all times."

It was a beautiful night for a walk. There was a soft onshore breeze, mild and fragrant. From every restaurant we passed wafted the most wonderful spiced scents. Every bar was packed. Everywhere there were fancy cars. There were lots of good-looking women. They were really beautiful: dark, slender and stylish—too hot for us. We made it to our restaurant after about half an hour. It was quite plain. In the corner was a big refrigerated display like you see in a meat market. It was filled to the brim with fish, all different kinds and sizes. We sat down at our table. Three waiters came over. George took charge. In three minutes, our table was covered with food and drinks.

"Would you fellows like to try *narghile?*"

"What's that, George?"

He pointed to another table where they were smoking water pipes. "Sure."

He got one of the waiters to come over and whispered in his ear. In another minute two guys came over, each one carrying a water pipe. They carried a small pot filled with red-hot coals, each about the size of your little finger. They filled the bowl of the pipe with what I guessed was tobacco and place several of the coals on top. Then they got the pipe smoking by holding the tip at the end of the hose in their fist so they didn't have to lip it. When it was adequately stoked, they handed off the mouthpiece to Willard and me. Neither one of us had ever smoked tobacco, so it was a pretty comical coughing extravaganza for the first few puffs.

"George, do they ever put anything else in these pipes?"

"They do sometimes. Mostly in Baalbek, though."

"Oh."

Of all the meals in all the wonderful restaurants in all the different cities where we had eaten so far, this was the best. There was no stopping the onslaught of items for consumption. I ate some local fish that literally cleaved itself off of the bones. We took frequent breaks from eating with beverages and *narghile*. At one point, I excused myself and went to the bathroom. I walked around the corner and saw one of our waiters.

"Hey, this is great. By the way, my friend and I were wondering if you might have any hash for our pipes."

"Oh, I am sorry, sir. I do not have anything like that here. I know where you might go, but, please, I cannot help you tonight."

"I am very sorry to have troubled you. I know it was rude. Please forgive me."

He looked at me, slowly eyeing me up and down.

"It is not that you were rude. Let me check with one of the other waiters. I will see if I can help you."

"Thank you very much."

I walked back to the table. Things were in full swing. George was unbelievable. No one could stay mad at him for more than two seconds. He had about five waiters, two *narghile* boys, and the chef going nonstop in serving our table. Every time that the water pipes went out, he called for help. This happened about every five minutes. After a while, one of the *narghile* boys just stayed at our table. I watched as the other one returned. He looked out of the corner of his eye at me until he noticed that I was looking at him. Then he placed some more fuel in the bowls, followed by a couple of coals.

"I hope that you enjoy this, sir. It is a different tobacco."

"I'm sure we will. Thank you very much."

I dug into my pocket and gave him a ten Lebanese pound note. I leaned across the table and whispered to Willard.

"Check this out, Willard. I think it's something special. Don't cough too hard."

We smoked through the bowl and at first it was hard to tell any difference. About halfway through, though, I started to feel high. It really did taste a little different too. All I know is that Willard started laughing uncontrollably. I was right behind him. I didn't think that anyone else noticed. It was already pretty smoky in there, and everyone else was drunk. Then George started getting wild. He got about three tables involved and introduced us to all of them. Next, he ordered up some dancing girls. I never figured out how he did it; there weren't any there before, and I wasn't sure where they came from. Our buddy kept bringing us more refills for the *narghile*. I lost track of whether it was regular or super, and by that time it didn't matter anyway. Abu Sultan just sat there with a big smile on his face. He was a nice guy.

We finished up and George called for the check. He whipped out his wad of $100 traveler's checks and signed a couple for the waiter. Willard and I each gave special tips to the *narghile* boys. George's last move was to have a group picture taken. When it came back, I didn't notice how fat I was. The staff called for a cab. We waited for only a minute, then one of those Mercedes cabs showed up. We all climbed in and headed for Al Hamra.

"Well, how do you like Beirut so far, Bill?"

"I've never had so much fun in my life, George. That meal was unbelievable. What a great restaurant. We're glad you picked that one, Abu Sultan."

I looked at Willard as I spoke the last sentence.

"What should we do now?"

"Let's do some dancing."

"We shall ask Abu Sultan again. Where is the hottest club?"

"I know just the place."

We were dropped off at a club with a long line trailing out the front door. George went right to the front of the line and spoke briefly with the fellow there. After a moment, he was waving to us to come. We all shuffled up, excusing ourselves to the other people. They didn't seem to mind. We walked through the door, and I saw George greasing palms left and right.

It was a pretty fancy place. There was some really good music playing on a huge stereo. It was rock and roll and some disco: Robin Trower, Led Zeppelin, lots of good stuff. We eased our way into the back, and George had one of the guys lead us to a table. It was right at the edge of the dance floor. The crowd was very lively. Whereas the Istanbul crowd was juvenile in their behavior, this crowd was sophisticated. The guys were very rich and dressed to the gills. The women were spectacular. There was heavy-duty jewelry everywhere. George was not intimidated. He was talking to about three girls at once. Anna was cool; her mother seemed to watch George more closely. Pretty soon George had set Willard and me up with some knockout babes. They grabbed our hands and led us onto the dance floor. They started dancing like I had never seen before. They were gyrating their whole bodies; everything was rhythmic and controlled. They were like professionals. We did our best and had a pretty good time. George was sitting at the table, talking to everybody. I got his attention and motioned to come on out and dance. He waved me off. By the time we got back to the table, our group had become the focus of the whole club.

"Are you friends of George?" one of our dancing friends asked me.

"Yeah, we're traveling together."

"Are you American?"

"Yes, how about you? Are you Lebanese?"

"Yes."

"You have a beautiful country, and you are a beautiful dancer."

"Thank you."

We sat down and our new friends joined us. George got the drinks going all around. It was pretty wild. The rest of the night was more of the same. We did a lot of dancing. I can't tell you how much fun it was. One of the guys we met took us outside for a couple of bowls of blonde hash. It was solid stuff. We came back in, and George gave us the head-back, squinty-eyes look. We just laughed. After much ado, we finally decided to go home. We exchanged phone numbers with our new friends and left in a cab.

"You're really something, George. I've probably never had this much fun with my boots on."

George laughed.

"I am glad you are here. We will have great fun."

We arrived back at the White House.

"Let's get some sleep. I have a big day planned for you tomorrow."

We all said good night, and Willard and I stumbled to our room and passed out on bare beds.

CHAPTER 14

The next morning, George came into our room and woke us up. I couldn't remember if I had locked the door or not.

"Come. Wake up. We have many things to do today."

"What time is it, George?"

"Eight o'clock."

"George!"

"I want to show you something special. Come upstairs when you are ready."

We got up and showered, then rode the elevator up to the sixth floor. George let us into his apartment. Anna had prepared a nice continental breakfast for us, Lebanese-style. It was pretty tasty, though I wasn't sure what it all was.

"I want to take you to a Palestinian refugee camp, to show you how the people are living. You will find it very interesting."

He kissed Anna good-bye and we went downstairs. The ladies said they were going to do a few things to fix up our apartment.

"First, I want to get some film for my camera. There is a camera store around the corner."

We walked catty-corner to the White House. The camera store was right in front of the alley where the second cab had dropped us off yesterday and from where we had spied the first cab. We walked in and George began to speak to the store owner in Arabic. After a few sentences, George started to look at us funny. The other fellow was looking at us and pointing and becoming pretty excited.

"You crazy sons of bitches!"

"What do you mean?"

The man continued to talk to him, and George would interject expletives at us intermittently.

"I can't believe you guys. You almost got yourselves killed!"

"What do you mean, George?"

"This man is saying that yesterday you were standing over in that alley, spying from around the corner at the Research Center."

"We weren't spying at the Research Center, George. We saw that cab driver, and we were watching him for a few minutes before we went over and talked to you."

The other guy continued to jabber excitedly.

"He says that he thought you were Israeli agents and that you were going to hit the Research Center."

"You've got to be kidding."

"He is not kidding. He almost shot you himself. He thought for sure that you would be shot by one of the guards."

Willard and I looked at each other with shocked faces. George talked to the guy and apparently told him our story. I wasn't sure that he believed it, but he finally started to calm down.

"He watched you spying from the alley for a few minutes, then saw you walk across the lot to the White House. He called the Research Center on the phone and alerted them to you. I hope that I can straighten this out with them."

I had never seen George so angry.

"We're sorry, George, we didn't know what we were doing. Is it going to be okay?"

"I don't know. I'll have to work on it. I'll have to talk to Abu Sultan."

"We didn't know that there was such a security situation here."

"There are many things that you do not know. You must be very careful here. People are very tense. The Israelis have attacked Kfarchouba, a village not far from here. We do not know what they will do next. Everyone is on the highest alert."

"George, you didn't tell us any of this when we were in Turkey."

"I did not know these things. Anyway, it won't affect you if you are careful and think before you do something stupid. You really do not know how close you came to dying yesterday. Please be careful and do not do anything foolish again without checking with me first."

George finally bought his film, and we asked him to apologize to the shopkeeper for us. He said some words to the man, who waved to us halfheartedly. I wasn't convinced of his sympathy or trust in us. We walked out.

"I do not think it would be a good time to go to the Palestinian camp. I would like to try to fix things about you guys first. Why don't you go into the city for the day, and I will find Abu Sultan. If you go up Al Hamra you will find plenty to do and see. Come back later in the day, and I will have everything straightened out. Do you need any money?"

"No thanks, George, we're all right. We're really sorry for all this trouble. We really didn't mean it."

"I know, fellas. It is just something that happened. Don't worry. But please be careful."

"We will."

We started walking up the street. I looked back and saw George walking back to the White House. It was a beautiful morning and was just beginning to get warm. The sun was strong. We walked by a couple of pinball arcades and stopped in one. It was a good one, and we were the only people there. We swapped about ten Lebanese pounds for tokens. I played some great games that I had not seen in America. The manager was very friendly.

"May I ask you something?"

"Of course."

"Are things safe in Beirut?"

"I think they are safe."

"Is there any danger of getting in trouble with the PLO or anything?"

"No. They keep to themselves. They are in camps at the edge of the city and beyond."

"What about the Research Center? Is it a dangerous place to be around?"

"I do not think so. I walk by it every day to work."

"Thank you."

We played all of our tokens and moved on down Hamra. Our next stop was a record store. We went in and began to look around. The shopkeeper was a young guy who spoke excellent English. The records were all in bins like in America, but they were in thick plastic jackets that had been opened up.

"Do you sell used records?"

"I could sell you records, but it is very expensive. I prefer to record tapes and sell them."

"That's a good idea. We could use a few new tapes."

Our collection of tapes was small, and we had memorized every selection. We looked through his stock and picked out some albums that we asked him to record for us: *Led Zeppelin*, Robin Trower *Bridge of Sighs*, and BTO. He told us to come back tomorrow and he would give us our tapes. We thanked him and kept on moving. Our walk carried us farther down Hamra. It was a good street. There was plenty of action. It was getting to be lunchtime, but I had an idea.

"Let's go swimming."

"Are you nuts?"

"Why not? It's warm enough, and I'm sure the water is perfect. Let's buy a couple of cheap bathing suits and towels. We can change in a hotel and go for a dip. Then we can eat lunch."

"Whatever you want, T."

We bought some extra-large suits and beach towels for a small amount of money, changed into them there at the shop, and walked out with our suits on under our pants. We asked which way to the beach, and the clerk pointed down the street. We followed his directions, turning a corner sharply to come to the water. It was beautiful. There were some low rocks at the water's edge and a beach farther down the shoreline. We threw our clothes off and went to the rocks. We both sat down with our feet dangling in the water for a few minutes. The water was warm enough, considering it was February. I was the first one to jump in and it was great. Willard rolled his corpulent body into the water. We had a good swim. The water was blue, clear, and was really just the right temperature. We swam for about half an hour. I was surprised that there was nobody else at the beach. I climbed back onto the rock that I had been sitting on and dangled my feet. Willard came up a minute later and heaved himself up onto an adjacent rock. Just then I felt something touch—almost grab— one of my feet. I shuddered and jerked my legs out of the water.

"Something just grabbed my leg, Willard!"

"You pussy. It's just a piece of seaweed."

"No, I'm serious. I felt it grab me."

"Right."

I looked down into the spot where my foot had been. Suddenly, a small tentacle came flopping up on the rock.

"Look, it's a fucking octopus!"

"Shit, you're right!"

We could see it clearly now. It was about two feet long. It was inking a little. I tried to grab it with one of my shoes, but I couldn't even get close to it.

"What the hell are you doing?"

"I'm trying to catch it."

"What for?"

"It's a delicacy. I'm sure we could sell it."

"You're really nuts. Come on. Let's get going. I can tell you're hungry."

"Thirsty too."

I made one more lunge for the octopus, but to no avail. I dived in the water one more time and swam around to a different rock. I climbed out and dried off, then we walked back to civilization. We had a great lunch right on the beachfront.

"Do you think we should go back?"

"Yeah, why not? I'm sure George has fixed everything."

We made our way back down Al Hamra. We passed a theater that was showing a Clint Eastwood movie: *Thunderbolt and Lightfoot*. We decided to go see it. It was in English with French and Arabic subtitles. It was a good movie with plenty of violence and good acting. They used a 105 mm recoilless rifle to blast open a safe. I wondered if the PLO had any of those weapons. The movie hadn't come out yet at the time I had left America; I thought it was pretty good for Beirut to get a first run American film so early. We went out into the late afternoon sun and walked back to the White House. It was a nice time for a walk.

We got back to our block. We walked to the White House. I didn't see any guards. We kind of hurried into the building and went to our apartment. I unlocked the door, and we went in. Our room looked completely different. It looked great. We now had sheets and blankets on the beds; a radio; glasses, plates, and silverware in the kitchen; and our clothes had been washed and put away into the dresser.

"This is unbelievable. Want a beer?"

"Sure."

I got us both a beer. I gave Willard his and walked into the bedroom. I noticed that our coats had been moved; my coat had been on the end and was now on the inside of Willard's. The bathroom had towels and soap and shampoo.

"Anna and her mom redid the whole place for us. They are so nice."

We went out on the veranda and sat down to drink our beers. I saw a guard. He waved to us, and we both waved back.

"I guess George fixed everything."

"Let's go find him and see what's going on."

We went upstairs and knocked on his door. He answered the door himself.

"My friends, you have returned. Come in."

We went inside and it smelled great. Anna must have been making something for supper.

"We had a nice day, George. How about you?"

"Not so bad. I think I worked everything out with the people at the Research Center."

"Great. The guard waved at us, so we figured that you had."

"It is all in the past. You have a good sense of timing; we are ready to eat. We have lots of food. I won't ask if you are hungry."

"You know we are."

We sat down to a wonderful meal. There was lamb; a finely diced, seasoned salad; crispy, spiced filling for the bread; yogurt; and some other stuff that I didn't recognize enough to describe. It was great. George was his old jovial self. We drank mineral water and wine.

"Tomorrow we will do what I had planned today for us."

"Are you sure it's okay, George? We don't want to cause you any more trouble."

"I am sure. What did you do today?"

"We had a blast. We played pinball—I've never seen so many pinball arcades in my life. Then we stopped at a record store where the guy is going to make us some tapes. Then we went swimming in the sea—I got grabbed by an octopus!"

"You're kidding. Are you all right?"

"He's fine, the little pussy. Then we went to a movie. It was a good day. Oh yeah. We had a nice lunch down on the water."

"You did have a good day. Should we do anything tonight?"

"It doesn't matter, George. What do you feel like?"

"I think we will stay home tonight. You fellas can be on your own tonight, or you can stay with us. You can use my car if you want, but you are right at the edge of where you want to be if you prefer to walk. Do what you like."

"Why don't we just cruise around Al Hamra, Willard? We don't need your car, George. Thanks for offering, though."

"Sure."

We thanked Anna for the wonderful meal and said good night.

"Be careful." George held onto Willard's hand while they were shaking and squeezed it as he spoke. Willard smiled through a grimace and squeezed back. George reached behind Willard's head and roughed up his hair. We all three laughed, and Willard and I turned out of the apartment. We walked down the hall to the elevator.

"What do you want to do?"

"I don't know."

"I have an idea."

"Yeah?"

"Let's call those girls and see if they want to go out."

"We don't have a car."

"So what? They can pick us up."

"Call them up."

We went down to the lobby and had the evening clerk place the call for us. Willard did the talking. One of them answered the phone and was very friendly. She said that they were going to a party. There would probably be Americans and there would certainly be some Lebanese people there, and she thought it would be okay if we went. The party was going to be about two blocks from our place.

"Perfect. Let's get ready."

After getting dressed, we sat out on the veranda and had a few beers. We had a chance to watch the area around the apartments and the Research Center. George was right. There were always three guys on duty. One guy either sat outside the front door or was just inside. Two others were constantly on patrol around the perimeter. They wore civilian clothes and the checkered headgear. I still thought it was pretty weird that a library needed three guards with machine guns around the clock.

She had given us directions to the party, so we took off walking. We were there in fifteen minutes. We could hear the music, so we followed it to an apartment on the third floor of a building not unlike the White House. We knocked and a very friendly Lebanese-looking fellow opened the door.

"Hello."

"Hello. We are friends of Myrna. She thought it would be okay if we came. I am Bob and this is Bill." I held out my hand.

"Oh, yes. I am Elias. You are friends of George. Please come in."

We walked into what was obviously his apartment. The party was pretty quiet. It was mostly a college or young professional crowd.

"Let me introduce you to some of my friends."

We soon met everyone there. It looked about three-quarters

Lebanese, and the balance divided between real Arab-looking types and Americans or Europeans.

"Where are you from?"

"We're both from Nevada, in America. Are you from Beirut, Elias?"

"Yes. I am a medical student at the American University. Are you from Las Vegas or Reno?"

"Reno. And we are both premed. How is medical school?"

"Not too bad. It is hard work but good. What are you doing in Beirut?"

"We're both on leave terms. Bill just finished a foreign study program in Germany, and I will start a similar program in April."

"Also in Germany?"

"Yes."

"Did you fly here?"

"No, we drove."

"From Germany?"

"Yes."

"You're kidding. That is a long trip."

"It really is. It is not a trip we care to take back."

"I don't blame you. How will you avoid it?"

"We're going to sell Bill's car."

"Oh, yes. We have a very good market here for cars. It is open every day. I suppose you will take your car there and sell it."

"We don't know exactly. We've already had one offer, but George is helping us so we're just going to do what he says."

"How did you meet George?"

"We met at the Greek-Turkish border, and he gave us some advice on what to buy at the duty-free store. We've been with him ever since, for the most part."

"He is a famous man. You are very lucky."

"Yeah. He has been really good to us. We've had a great time."

"I am glad that you came here tonight. I hope that you have some fun."

"Elias, can I ask you something?"

"Sure."

"Why is it that Iraqis cannot enter Syria?"

"They can."

"Are you sure?"

"Yes, of course. Why do you ask?"

"We had understood that they were not allowed to enter Syria."

"That is not true."

I looked around for Willard. I was sure he would be interested in this bit of trivia. He was talking to some girl.

"Thanks. Oh, one other thing. Is Beirut safe?"

"Safer than New York City," he laughed.

"That isn't saying much. Is it really safe?"

"It is safe. There are some troubling events going on around us, but Beirut is a safe city. It is regarded as home by many different people. It is respected as an open city. No one would disturb that. You do not have to worry here."

I walked over to Willard and stood by him. Willard introduced me to the girl. She looked like an American.

"Nancy, this is my good friend Bob. T, this is Nancy Johnson."

"How are you?"

"Nice to meet you."

"Are you an American?"

"Yes. I'm from Andover, Mass."

"No kidding. I used to live in Natick."

"Huh. My brother lives in Natick."

"What are you doing in Beirut?"

"I work for Citybank."

"Hmm. That sounds like a good job."

"It is. I've been having a good time. Beirut is a great city. How long have you guys been here?"

"Just a few days."

"You'll have a great time. Let me know if I can do anything for you. See you later. I need to talk to a friend of mine."

She walked away to another corner of the apartment.

"Thanks, T. Your charm is irresistible, as usual."

"Sorry, Willard . . . hey, I learned something interesting. Iraqis can go into Syria anytime they want."

"Great. What do you think that means?"

"Either George lied to us or there is another reason that he cannot enter Syria."

"Or both."

"Oh well. It doesn't matter . . . you know, Elias is a nice guy. He's in med school at the American University of Beirut."

"Maybe we can go here after we don't get in in the States."

"Yeah right."

"I heard you guys are Americans. I'm Peter Lange."

We introduced ourselves and shook hands. He was a tall, handsome guy about our age. I couldn't detect any identifying accent.

"I work for Pan Am. Are you guys students?"

"Yeah. We're on a break from a foreign study program in Germany."

"Great. By the way, have you had a chance to sample any of the local hash?"

"Just a little. But we wouldn't mind trying out some more."

"There's some here. The only thing is, they roll it up in tobacco cigarettes, in trumpets. It helps if you smoke."

"We tried out something like that and survived. We went to a restaurant and smoked some in a water pipe."

"Oh yeah, they'll do that for you sometimes if they like you. Come on."

We stepped out on the veranda. Half of the party had migrated there. They were passing around two of the trumpets. I took a hit and almost fell down. Willard did the same.

"Pretty good, eh?"

"Yeah," I answered through a whirling tobacco buzz.

"Look, here is Myrna now."

Myrna and Elizabeth came into the party together, and all eyes were on them. They were beautiful. They came out on the porch and said hi to everyone, then came around and stood next to Willard and me.

"Thanks a lot for inviting us here tonight, Myrna. That was really nice. Good to see you."

"It is good to see you. Did you survive the other night?"

"Barely."

She laughed, "Me too." We smoked a few more trumpets, and everyone got pretty high. Elias turned up the music, and people went inside and started dancing. I danced with Myrna once, then about five horny Lebanese guys started buzzing around like hornets. I wanted to be a good guest, so I excused myself and said I would see her later. I saw Nancy standing there so I went over to her.

"I forgot that I wanted to ask you something. My freshman roommate is from North Andover. I wonder if you might know him. Ted Macum."

"Ted Macum. Ted Macum. Is he a skinny guy with black hair and glasses, real smart?"

"That's him."

"Yeah. My brother was on the same soccer team with him or something. Do you go to Dartmouth?"

"That's right."

"Yeah, I know who he is. He's a nice guy. That's funny. Small world, again."

"Yeah, I think it happens all the time . . . say, I wanted to ask you, do you feel safe here?"

"Pretty safe. The local guys are really horny and grabby, but they're harmless. There are some problems politically right now, but nothing overt. We get bulletins from the American embassy all the time. There is some crazy stuff going on right now."

"Like what?"

"Like the Israeli invasion into southern Lebanon. Like the fishermen's strike. Like an interior minister who was assassinated. Things like that. Nothing really related or continuous, but weird stuff. You should check into the embassy and let them know that you are here."

"Really?"

"It's no big deal. It would just be a good thing to do."

"Okay. Thanks."

"How long are you going to be here?"

"Just a few weeks, I think."

"Oh, well, you'll be okay."

We stayed at the party for a little while longer. It started to break up when Myrna and Elizabeth said they would be going. They came over to us before they left.

"We have to go now. It was nice seeing you both again."

"It was our pleasure. Thanks again for inviting us. Elias is a nice guy."

"Yes, he is," Myrna said, "he is my cousin."

"That explains it."

"That explains what?"

"That he's a nice guy."

"Oh, thank you."

"Maybe we can see you again; maybe we can go out some time."

"That would be nice. Give us a call. Good night."

"Good night."

Willard and I hung around for a few more minutes, then went over to Elias to thank him and say good night. He was very gracious.

"I hope to see you again. Thank you for coming here tonight."

We said good-bye to the other residual creatures and walked out into the night.

"That was fun. Now back to the White House home for wayward boys."

"I wonder what that fucking George is up to."

"Yeah. Me too. I think he's always up to something."

"I think they're all always up to something here. We better stay on our toes."

"Sure. But I'm not sure that's enough."

"We'll see."

We walked home through the Beirut night, quietly and carefully, and went to bed with a little more on our minds than before. I couldn't stop wondering why George had lied to us about his not having been able to get into Syria.

CHAPTER 15

We were awakened the next morning by a sound that we hadn't heard in a while, a soft rain on the window.

"Oh shit, it's raining."

"So much for our tropical paradise."

"I wonder what George has in mind for us."

"I think he wants to take us to a PLO refugee camp."

"Swell."

"I'm not sure we should go. All we need is to get into another jam with the PLO."

"Oh well. Let's see what he has to say first."

We showered and got dressed, then went to the lobby and had the clerk ring George's room.

"What did you fellas do last night?"

"We went to a party."

"Great."

"It was Myrna's cousin, Elias. He's a nice guy."

"Let's go see the PLO camp."

"Are you sure we should go, George? Haven't we already done enough with the PLO?"

"What do you mean?"

"I mean with the people at the Research Center. Don't they already think that we're suspicious?"

"I told you that I worked that out. They understand that you are just students. I told them why you were sneaking around. They laughed when I told them the story. Don't worry. I think it is important for you to see how the Palestinian people are forced to live."

"Okay. When do you want to go?"

"I will be down to get you in fifteen minutes."

"Do we need our passports?"

"No. I don't think so."

"Are you sure?"

"I am sure. They'll know me. See you."

He hung up and I told Willard the plan.

"Oh well. It's been nice knowing you, T."

"Come on, Willard. It'll be interesting. You've got to admit, George hasn't steered us wrong yet."

"I don't know. . . . You know, I wonder how my car is doing."

"Let's tell him we want to go see it."

"Okay."

"And let's try to find out why he never came to Syria."

"Oh, who cares?"

"I don't know. I just wonder."

"Yeah. Me too."

George came down and we walked over to the pimpmobile. "You fellas will really like this. I am very excited."

"George." I hesitated.

"Yes, Bill."

MEET ME IN BEIRUT

"Why did you really not go to Syria?"

"I told you. I could not get in."

"Yeah, but why not? Iraqis can go into Syria if they want to."

"Who told you this?"

"Everybody."

"It is a long story."

"Just tell us the short version."

"It is because I am PLO."

"They know you're PLO?"

"They might have known. I could not take the chance."

"You knew all along that you wouldn't meet us in Damascus, didn't you?"

"I wasn't sure. It was only after we separated that I was sure that I could not go to Damascus. I learned it in Cyprus."

"Come on, George, this sounds like a bunch of bullshit. Just tell us the truth."

"I am telling you the truth. In Cyprus I learned that I could not go into Syria. This is the truth."

"Can you tell us why you learned it in Cyprus?"

"I was told that it would not be safe for me to go to Syria."

"Why?"

"The Syrians are very hard right now. If you want to know the truth, I was almost surprised that you were able to get in yourselves. But I knew you could do it. You guys are special. You can do anything you want."

"Except figure out what the hell is going on."

"There is nothing to figure out, and nothing is going on. Once again, I ask you to trust me. I have not yet let you down, have I?"

"You mean except for Damascus?"

"I told you. There was a good reason for that, and I will always be sorry that I did not meet you there. I can say nothing else but ask you to trust me."

"We do trust you, George. But you have to understand where we're coming from. There's a lot we don't understand."

"That is why I want you to see a PLO camp. You will understand things better after that. Things are very different here than in other places. Don't worry."

"Okay."

We weren't totally convinced. I could tell by the look on Willard's face that he was incredulous. We would go with George to the camp, though, and learn about his PLO.

"By the way, George, how's my car doing?"

"It is going well. It will be ready in two days, and then we will sell it."

"Do you think we could go see it?"

"If you wish. But it is not ready yet."

"I know. But I still want to see it."

"Fine. After we see the camp."

We had been driving for a few miles, past the nice part of town into areas that looked pretty run-down.

"Are we getting close?"

"We are almost there. This is the largest camp near Beirut, and there are several. They may ask you some questions. Just tell them the truth."

"Oh boy."

We pulled up to large stacks of sandbags at each end of a long metal gate. The perimeter was marked by a ragtag fence of barbed wire, sandbags, and common junk. At the gate were two soldiers, dressed like our friends back at the Research Center, with automatic weapons. They peered into the car, and the one on George's side talked with George in Arabic for a few minutes. They seemed to reach some conclusion and opened up the gate and waved us in. They directed us to a corner of the area and we parked. A soldier wearing a uniform came walking up to us from a building in the compound about seventy-five feet away.

"Do they know you, George?"

"No."

Willard and I looked at each other.

"They want to know why we don't have our passports."

"You gotta be kidding."

"I am serious."

"George!"

The soldier walked up and talked with George again. He waved us toward the building.

"He wants to ask us a few questions inside."

"Do you think we could just leave instead, George?"

"No. Don't worry. This will not take long."

We walked up some stairs into a low wooden building. Inside was a full-fledged army camp, with soldiers and masses of weapons: automatic rifles, handguns, machine pistols, hand grenades, a couple of mortars—everything you would need for a war. We all sat down in the main room.

"Who are you?"

"I am George Tanjanian." George then looked at me.

"I am Bob Tibolt." I looked at Willard.

"I am Bill Bromley." Willard wasn't looking at anybody.

The head soldier looked at me: "Why are you here?"

"George wanted us to see a PLO refugee camp."

"This is not a refugee camp. This is an army base," he barked. He was very angry.

"I am sorry. I just meant that he wanted us to see where Palestinians live. He said that in America we did not see things the way they really are here."

"You are American?"

"Yes, we are." Willard pointed to himself and me.

The head soldier stepped up from his desk and walked out of the room. He spoke briefly with some other soldiers in the hall, then returned.

"Would you please come with me?" He motioned in my direction. I got up and followed him out of the room. I could see Willard and George each heading out of the room in different directions down the hall. I followed the head soldier into another office. He held the door for me, then closed it behind me.

"May I search you?"

"Yes."

He frisked me thoroughly, then pointed to a chair in front of a desk. I sat down and he walked behind the desk. Before he sat down, he pulled a huge 9 mm automatic cannon out from a holster in the back of his belt, placed it into the desk drawer, then closed the drawer slowly. He took a pack of cigarettes out of his breast pocket and placed it on the desk.

"Cigarette?" he offered as he lit one.

"No, thanks, I don't smoke."

He got out a pen and sheet of paper.

"What is your full name?"

"Robert Earl Tibolt."

"What is your father's full name?"

"Robert Alexander Tibolt."

"What is your mother's name?"

"Jeanne Church."

"Where do you live?"

"Reno, Nevada, USA."

"How long have you lived there?"

"Nine years."

"What is your job?"

"I am a student."

"Where are you a student?"

"Dartmouth College, Hanover, New Hampshire, USA."

"How long have you known your friends?"

"I have known Bill for six years."

"What is his full name?"

"William Bromley."

"What is his mother's name?"

"Joan Bromley."

"How long have you known George?"

"About a month."

"Where did you meet?"

"At the duty-free shop at the Greek-Turkish border."

"What are you doing here?"

"In Beirut?"

"Yes."

"Just being a tourist."

"When did you leave America?"

"December thirty-first."

"Where did you go?"

"Stuttgart. Germany."

"How long were you there?"

"Uh, one week."

"Then where did you go?"

"Bill and I went to Munich."

"You were with Bill?"

"Yes, I have been with Bill since I arrived from America."

"Then where did you go?"

"Then we went to Yugoslavia."

"How do you travel?"

"In Bill's car."

"That one?" He pointed outside.

"No; it is a VW square back. It is being repaired."

"Where did you go in Yugoslavia?"

"We drove the length of the country, but we stayed in Dubrovnik."

"How long?"

"About four days."

"Then where did you go?"

"Thessaloniki."

"How long did you stay there?"

"Ten days."

"Why did you stay there so long?"

"We got in a wreck."

"Then you met George?"

"Yes."

"You already knew him."

"No. We met him for the first time."

"You knew who he was."

"No. Uh-uh. He just drove up and we started talking."

"I see."

"Where did you go after Turkey?"

"Syria."

"Why Syria?"

"It's on the way to Beirut."

"Where did you go in Syria?"

"Hama and Homs and Damascus."

"How long were you in Damascus?"

"Three weeks."

This continued on for a long, long time. He learned a lot about me. He had smoked about half the pack of cigarettes. I was almost sick from the smoke and the tension. I felt a little faint.

"May I have something to drink and some fresh air?"

"Soon."

"Where did you go after Damascus?"

"We drove here to Beirut."

"When was that?"

"About a week ago."

"Where are you staying?"

"The White House Apartments."

His eyes lit up, and he looked at me very hard.

"Excuse me, please."

He stepped out of the room and left the door open. There was another soldier right out in the hall. I felt like shit. He came back in about five minutes.

"Would you come with me, please?"

"Yes."

We walked down the hall, back to the central room. George was already sitting there. I sat down, and the officer who had interviewed me sat down at the desk.

"Bob, how long were you in Munich?"

"About three days."

"And how long did it take you to get to Dubrovnik?"

"About another week."

"George, where did you meet Bob?"

"In Turkey."

"Where?"

"At the border."

"Where did you go after that?"

"We went to lunch."

"Where?"

"Babaeski."

"Then where did you go?"

"Istanbul."

"How long did you stay there, Bob?"

"About five days."

Just then Willard was escorted in by another soldier. He didn't look too good. He was really pale.

"Bill, what is your father's name?"

"William Bromley."

"What is Bob's father's name?"

"I don't know."

"You don't know?"

"No. He doesn't live in Reno, and I have never met him."

"What is his mother's name?"

"Jeanne Church."

"How long have you and Bob known each other?"

"About five years."

"How long have you known George?"

"About seven or eight weeks."

"Where did you meet him?"

"At the border of Greece and Turkey."

"Then where did you go?"

"Istanbul."

"You didn't stop for lunch?"

"No . . . uh, yes. We did stop for lunch."

"How long were you in Istanbul?"

"Four or five days."

"Bob says that you stayed in Istanbul for two weeks."

"Yeah, I guess we were. No. Wait a minute . . . God, I'm not sure."

George had been listening closely, and he casually corrected the interrogator's intentional mistake: "No, he didn't say that; Bob said we were there for five days."

"Oh, yeah, that's right. I remember now."

We started to laugh.

"You shut up!" The officer was very angry that his interrogation ploy had been foiled. He stood up and walked out of the room. I looked at George and gave him a really fucked-up look. He kind of shrugged his shoulders. Willard was still pretty shook. We didn't talk.

The head officer came back.

"We would like to ask that you come with us to another station. There are several more things that we would like to check."

He looked at George.

"We have tried to call the White House Apartments. There is no answer. Would you please come?"

We walked out of the building into two waiting Mercedes cabs. One of the officers rode in back with Willard, and I rode shotgun. George rode by himself in the front seat of the other cab, with another soldier in the back. We followed one another for several miles, through neighborhoods that we hadn't seen before. Willard and I didn't speak or look at each other. We arrived at what seemed to be another camp. We stopped at a gate, then were waved through. We were escorted into another building like the last. This one was bigger and had more soldiers and more hardware. We were all shunted into different rooms and interrogations like the last ones took place. I was really getting sick. We had not eaten, I was kind of hungover, I was thirsty, and starting to get scared. And they all were blowing cigarette smoke in my face. Here we were merely questioned and were not brought back together to have our facts cross-checked. We were then asked to get into some more cabs and were ferried across town again.

We stopped in front of an old building in an urban area and were discharged through a crowd to the offices upstairs. I could tell that this was headquarters. There were several teletypes, numerous telephones, a large radio occupying half a wall, and lots of office staff working. We were led to the back of the office and up an elevator. I was sure the others were also wondering what our fate that we were so rapidly approaching now would be. We all sat down in an office. The door was closed behind us.

"What's going on, George?"

"I am not sure."

"Are we safe?"

"Yes. That I am sure."

"I'm about ready to puke my guts out."

"I understand."

Just then the door opened and a man walked in. He was obviously one of the superiors of the organization. He was tall and muscular and not as dark as most of the rest of them. He walked up to each one of us, spoke our names, and shook our hands warmly.

"I wish to apologize for the inconvenience that we have caused you today. I am sure you understand that we have our reasons for being so careful. My comrades whom you met initially were disturbed by your lack of passports, and we could not let you go until we cleared you and were sure of your identities. We spoke with Abu Sultan at the White House Apartments. He confirmed everything. George, I am sorry that we did not recognize you earlier. We know of the help that you have so freely given to our struggle in the past. Please forgive our lack of hospitality. I hope that you understand."

"Of course we understand. It is really my fault that we did not have passports. I wanted my friends to have a chance to learn about the PLO firsthand, because I know that in America, they have very little chance to hear the truth."

"We appreciate your trying to inform our American friends about our struggle. Perhaps another day you could return to one of our bases for a guided tour. Please let me know when you might like to do that."

He reached into his drawer and took out three copies of a magazine, *Palestine—P.L.O. Information Bulletin*. It was Volume 1, Number 1, January–February 1975. It had a picture of Arafat on the cover. He gave each of us a copy.

"I hope that you will read this. It will give you some perspective on our plight. I am sure that you wish to return to the White House. It has been a long day. Please accept these magazines and our best wishes."

He showed us to the door and led us downstairs to a waiting cab. He never did say his name.

"May I ask you again, Bob, when were you in Damascus?"

"Uh, I think for three weeks—during the last week of February into the first two weeks of March."

"Is that right, Bill?"

"Yes, I think so."

"Very good. I wish you well."

He shook our hands and kissed George. We climbed into the cab and the driver took off for the first base where we had left George's car.

"Well, that was bitchin', George."

"I am very sorry. It was an unpleasant experience for you."

"I can't fucking believe that we were interrogated by the PLO for six fucking hours. That sucked."

"I do not understand why they harassed us."

"We had no passports, we're already suspects for being spies, the Israelis have invaded Lebanon, and the interior minister was assassinated. I'm sure they're in a state of fucking war. Shit, George. That was a bunch of bullshit."

"I really expected them to recognize me and to show us some hospitality."

We drove back to the White House. I had never seen George drive so slowly. We were met at the door by Abu Sultan. He started banging away at George the second that we arrived. He was pissed. I didn't know why he was so mad, but I sure felt the same way.

CHAPTER 16

We had gone to bed, slept for twelve hours, and awakened the next day. It was apparently the monsoon season. Another day came upon us shrouded in grey and laced with a driving rain.

"We may have seen the last of the sun, Willard."

"Oh well, it was nice while it lasted."

"I wonder what George has in mind for us today."

Willard gave me a real hard look. "Don't ask."

We both started laughing.

"I can't believe that crazy fucker."

"Call his ass up."

"What's the rush?"

"You're right."

We stayed in bed. We probably slept another hour. I got up and took a shower. We had a few food items in the refrigerator. I used some eggs and bread and made an omelet and toast. Willard got out of bed when he smelled the food. It was pretty tasty.

"Take a shower and I'll call George."

"Okay."

I went out to the lobby and called George. "Hello, George."

"Hello, Bill."

"How are you?"

"Good. What do you want to do today?"

"I thought we might go visit the PLO."

"Bill!"

"Just kidding. What do you want to do, George? We're easy."

"Let's drive around. Maybe your car is ready. We can also do some shopping."

"Okay."

"See you in fifteen minutes."

I went back to the room. Willard was doing the dishes.

"You're going to make somebody a good wife someday."

"Fuck you. What did George say?"

"I told him we wanted to go to a PLO camp."

Willard didn't even smile.

"No, he wants to drive around, maybe go shopping. He said your car might be ready."

"Great."

"Get ready."

George came down to our apartment and walked in. "I learned that your car is ready, Bob. Would you like to go and get it?"

"Sure. . . . Do we have to pay for it?"

"I will pay for it, and you can pay me back when you sell it."

"Are you sure, George?"

"I am sure."

"How much is it going to be?"

"About three hundred dollars."

"That ain't bad."

"How do we sell it?"

MEET ME IN BEIRUT

"We will take it to the market for used cars."

"When are you going to sell your car?"

"I am not sure. I think when I am ready to leave Beirut."

"Where will you go next?"

"I may stay here. There is much money here, and much money to be made."

"I guess we have to start thinking about getting back too."

"You just got here. What do you mean?"

"I don't know; I've been overseas for six months. I'm about ready to go back."

"How about you, Bill?"

"I have some more time."

Willard gave me a dirty look. "You're staying with me, buddy. I have to get my money from you so I can get back to the States."

"I know."

"Why don't you both stay for a while? You will not find a better place to have fun, and I know a way to make some good money."

Willard and I looked at each other.

"How, George?"

"I will show you when we are out today."

We climbed into George's car, the three of us, and drove off. We followed a different course to the body shop where we had left Willard's car. It was parked out front. It looked brand new. Willard and I walked up to it. Willard walked around it twice.

"I can't fucking believe it, George. It's beautiful."

"I told you that they would do a good job."

"Yeah, but this looks brand new. They must have painted the whole thing."

He was right. The entire body had received a new paint job. There was also a brand-new rack on top; it looked like a small luggage rack, but it was made of plain steel, not chrome, and it had numerous screw holes in the frame.

"What's this, George?" Willard fingered the rack on the roof.

George asked the body man.

"He says it is a luggage rack. They are very popular here and will help us sell the car."

"Oh."

I stuck my head in the passenger window. Everything was clean and looked brand new.

"This is great, George. Your friends are artists."

I smiled broadly and shook hands with the main man. He returned a big smile and handshake. George spoke with him for a few minutes. I didn't see George give him any money, but the man gave George the keys and slapped him on the back.

"So. We are done. Shall we drive ourselves back to the White House?"

"Sure."

We followed George out of the lot, into the alley, and onto the streets of Beirut. He was his usual self again. Willard barely kept up. The car was running pretty good. I did notice some loose wires coming through the crack between the ceiling material and the roof. I guessed that they had come out when they popped the windshield back in. We were following George on a main drag. It was raining pretty hard. We noticed a street vendor. He had laid out a whole display of water pipes. We flashed our lights and blinked our horns at George. He finally saw us and pulled over. We pulled up next to George and rolled down the window. We were about a hundred yards past the stand.

"Hey, George, we want to buy a *narghile* back there."

"Okay."

"Let us try to bargain with the guy this time, okay, George?"

"Of course."

We turned around and drove back. The fellow was sitting under an umbrella, a large one that you might see at a beach. In front of him he had a selection of three different water pipes. He also had sets of the various Arabic headgears lined up in plastic bags; they were laid out on a tarp, and he had stretched another tarp from some poles to protect them from the rain. He was very happy to see us.

"*Marhaba.*"

"*Ahlan.*"

"Do you wish to buy something?"

"No, we are just looking. How much is this one?" I was handling the largest water pipe.

"Twenty-five pounds."

I made a very sour face to George.

"And this?" I showed him one of the Palestinian head wraps.

"Ten pounds."

"Hmm."

"This is too expensive. What else can you show us?"

He brought out some of the golden, tubular, woven head wrap retainers that the Saudis wear and waved them in my face.

"Ten pounds."

"For this, this, and this I will give you fifteen pounds."

"That is not possible. I buy them for more than that. I can sell them to you for thirty pounds."

"Two sets of those items for thirty pounds."

"I will sell you two of each for forty-five pounds all together."

I looked at Willard.

"Let's go."

We turned around and walked through the rain to our cars. The vendor followed us to the car and chattered about the cost of his goods. We climbed in and ignored him. George started his car and angled slowly into the street. As we started our car, the man banged on my window and motioned us back to the display. I rolled down my window.

"All right. All right. Thirty pounds for the six items."

I smiled at Willard.

"This is easy."

CHAPTER 17

George helped us load the things into the back of our car. "I thought of something that I want to show you guys. Follow me."

"Are we going any place that we need our passports?"

"No." He laughed and turned to get in his car. We followed him for a few miles through some commercial areas before he stopped. We all go out in the rain.

"What do you think?"

"About what, George?"

We were standing in front of a car wash.

"This." He pointed to the car wash.

"What about it?"

"This is my idea to make money. It is a great idea. It could make us all much money. This is the latest type of car wash. It is all automatic. I know a great location that I will show you."

"Besides making us stand out in the rain, why are we having this conversation, George? We're students in America. I could no more stay and run a car wash than fly without an airplane."

"You do not have to stay and run it. I would do that. You could be investors."

"I don't think you need my kind of investment, George. Let's go talk about this somewhere dry."

"Sure. Follow me back to the White House."

"Is he nuts?" I asked Willard after we got in the car. "He can't possibly think that we can help him. He must think that we're rich."

"I don't know why he would think that. I think he's crazy. We should probably think about getting out of here. I have to get back home."

"Yeah, I know. Let's talk to him about selling the car. Then we can leave. Things are a little weird here anyway."

We met George back in the lobby.

"Let's go talk in our apartment, George. We're going to grab a beer."

We walked in, grabbed a couple of cold ones from the refrigerator, and sat down.

"Who keeps cleaning this place? Every time we come in, things have been moved around."

"I have a maid come into your apartment and mine. I hope it is okay."

"Yeah, sure; thanks, George."

"Have you guys been having a good time?"

"The best. Everything you said about Beirut is true. We're glad we came here. . . . You know, though, we have to start making plans for going back to Germany. We need to sell our car."

George went to the refrigerator and got a beer.

"I'm sorry, George. I didn't know you wanted one." I had never seen him have a drink before.

"I know you cannot stay here forever. We can start selling your car tomorrow. It will not take long. . . . As you know, one of the reasons I wanted you to come here was so that you could learn about the Palestinian people. I am sorry that we had such a problem when we tried to go to one of their camps. We can go back some other time."

"I'm not sure that we want to go back, George. Why don't you just tell us about the Palestinians and the PLO. That might do for starters."

"I will do that. I am not an expert, but I know some things. I think you must know that Palestine was a land of about half a million people in the late 1800s. Most of the people were either Muslim or Christian, with only about 20,000 Jewish. By the end of World War I, over 50,000 European Jews had settled in Palestine. Britain oversaw this as part of its imperialistic plan in this area. They issued something called the Balfour Declaration that promoted this illegal immigration. Britain also received a mandate from the League of Nations to control Palestine. They controlled and gave away to Zionist Jews something that was not theirs to give."

"What is Zionism, George? I've heard of it, but I don't know what it is."

"It is the effort to place Jews in Palestine. In reality, it is imperialist, colonialist, and racist. I will talk more about it. By 1947, the number of Jews in Palestine was 600,000, compared to 1.25 million Palestinians. Jews owned about six percent of the arable land. The General Assembly of the United Nations approved a recommendation to divide Palestine, another example of people who had no right to exercise any authority giving away something that didn't belong to them. They gave over half of the land of Palestine to the Zionists. This was not good enough for the Zionist imperialists, so they began a war of terrorism against the civilian Arab people. In doing so, they occupied over eighty percent of Palestine; took over five hundred Arab towns, destroyed almost four hundred of them and built their settlements on the ruins of Arab Palestinians. Since that time, they have received limitless support from America that has allowed them to wage four wars against neighboring Arab countries. They have expanded their area of occupation several times as a result of these wars. Since 1947, over 30,000 Palestinians have died in the struggle. That would be the same as if six million Americans had died fighting someone who was trying to occupy and divide your country. Have you ever heard of any of these things?"

"It's all new to me, George."

"Me too."

"That is the history of the Palestinian problem. The new chapter began on January 1, 1965, when the Palestinian revolution was started. Since then, it has been the PLO and Yasser Arafat who have carried the battle and the message. It is a very difficult struggle, mostly because America keeps the Zionists supplied with the latest weaponry and lots of money. It hurts your own economy to do this."

"How did you get involved with the PLO, George? You're not a Palestinian, are you?"

"No, I told you I am Iraqi. Actually, I am Armenian. I learned about the PLO here in Beirut. Before 1970 the PLO was based in Jordan, but because of political problems, they had to leave there. They moved to Lebanon and Beirut and have been here since. I have been coming to Beirut for a long time, and I met some of their people. I have since tried to help them in any small way that I can."

"Why do they have to live as refugees?"

"They have no home; they have nowhere else to go. They are scattered around many Arab countries, and there are some left in Israel. In all of these places they are treated like second-class citizens. They have had their homeland stolen from them and they are now refugees. It is the only way they can live."

"What's going on with them now?"

"Many things. Too many things. Arafat gave a very important speech in November of last year to the UN. After that, there were ten days of mass uprisings by Palestinians in occupied territory. Israeli troops and police used very brutal means to break it up. Two young girl demonstrators were killed by tanks and weaponry. Hundreds of people were arrested, tried, and sentenced overnight. Before and since that time, PLO commandos have struck at strategic targets in Israel. Abu Sultan himself was wounded on a suicide raid to Nahariya; he was the only one of the squad to escape. You have also seen other commandos around here in the last few weeks. And the Israelis have struck back. They have used air strikes on Palestinian camps here in Beirut and in other parts of Lebanon. They have shelled the southern slopes of Mount Hermon, a town called Nabatieh, and Palestinian camps near there. We do not know when or where they will strike next. We have to rely on our intuition and limited intelligence efforts to stay one step ahead of them."

"This is all very interesting, George. How come we never heard about any of it?"

"Do you mean in America, or from me?"

"Well, I meant in America."

"The American news system is controlled by the Jews. You will never hear any part of the Palestinian side. This I can promise you."

I felt kind of bad about the whole thing. I was amazed again that the people around here didn't hate me for being an American. I felt even worse when Willard spoke again.

"Can we talk about the car? I need to sell it, George. There's no way we can drive that thing back. For one thing, we don't have the real papers with us. For another thing, it's just too far to drive."

"You showed me the papers. What do you mean you don't have them?"

"That was just the insurance paper. Your friend said it would work, though, right?"

"Yes, I'm sure it will."

"What do we have to do to sell it?"

"We will go to the market tomorrow. I will also look into selling my car. I am not ready to sell it, but I will begin the process. Maybe tonight we can get a good night's sleep."

He finished his beer and got up to leave. "You will see. We will sell your car for much money. Leave it to me."

"Don't worry, George. We will."

"Good night, my brudders."

"Good night, George." He gave us each a hug and left the room.

"What do you want to do for dinner?"

"Anything."

"Let's walk around Hamra."

"Okay."

We left the room and walked into the steady drizzle and artificial lights of the street. We were pretty familiar with the neighborhood. We stopped in a local joint that we had seen; it looked like a place where the locals would hang out. It was a small restaurant and bar. We went into the bar and bellied up. We sat next to a couple of older men. They were very well dressed, olive-skinned, and speaking Arabic. They regarded us politely by nodding. I spoke to them in English.

"Good evening, gentlemen."

"Good evening."

"How is the food here?"

"Not as good as the whiskey."

"Four whiskeys, then." I felt like a big shot. Willard gave me a most disgusted look.

We began talking to them. They were Lebanese businessmen. One worked for Air France and the other worked for a bank. I got the feeling that they had other financial interests as well.

"Could you tell us a few things about Beirut?"

"You are asking a lot; it is difficult to understand Beirut, let alone explain it. But go ahead and ask."

"Is it safe here?"

They looked at each other and shrugged.

"It is safe. Sometimes it is dangerous. I think it is getting more dangerous."

"Why do you say that?"

"There is too much going on. There are the Christians and the Muslims, the Israelis and the PLO, there are strikes and battles. I am worried about the future. Even your embassy has been warning its citizens to report to them daily."

"What?"

"I am serious. Have they not contacted you?"

"I don't think they know our address." I looked with incredulity at Willard.

"How did things get this way? We had heard that Beirut is the most beautiful city in the world. Is it changing?"

"It may be changing. It has always been a difficult balance here. Do you know anything of the history of Beirut?"

"Not at all."

"It could be said that the modern history began in 1943 with the National Pact. This was an effort to establish a stable government that included all of the members of our population. The Lebanese president would be a Maronite Christian, the prime minister Sunni Muslim, the speaker of parliament Shiite Muslim, and the parliament would be six-to-five Christian to Muslim. This ratio reflected the population at the time. It worked well until this decade. Then the population changed; Christians only made up one-third of the people, and the Muslims and Druse made up two-thirds. Shiites formed the largest single community. Efforts to change the balance were resisted by the Maronites.

They formed private armies to protect their interest. Pierre Gemayel founded the Phalangists that were led by his son Bachir. President Camille Chamoun founded the Tigers that were led by his son Dany.

"Things probably would have been okay—they would have been the same as always—but for the Palestinians and the Jews. Arafat and his PLO were kicked out of Jordan in 1970. They came to Beirut and other areas, mostly in southern Lebanon. This brought the attention of Israel. The PLO was welcomed by Muslims and Druse. The Christians wanted the Lebanese army to break up the PLO and make them leave. This led to a political deadlock, which we are still bound in. I do not know what will happen."

Things were all a little confusing for me. Now it was my turn to be the ugly American.

"Can you tell us how to sell our car?"

"This is not a good time."

"What do you mean? We've heard that Beirut has an excellent market for used cars."

"It was a wonderful place to sell used cars. People would drive cars here from all over Europe and other places to sell them here."

Willard and I looked at each other.

"Why do you say it *was* a wonderful place to sell cars?"

"Because they just tripled the tax on used car sales. This has seriously threatened the market. No cars are being sold."

"You're shittin' me!"

"I am not lying, if that is what you mean."

"When did this happen?"

"This week."

"I can't fucking believe it; we should have sold it to that hotel guy on the first day."

"What kind of car do you have?"

"It's a '71 VW square back with a luggage rack."

"Oh. I am sorry but you may have a difficult time selling it now. For example, my bank will not loan any more money on a used car purchase."

"I wonder if George knows this."

"I doubt it. He didn't act like he knew. He was still sure we could sell our car easy. He also wants to sell his. This is not good."

"Do you have any other news or advice for us? You have been very helpful."

"Only that you should stay in touch with your embassy; they may know something that the rest of us do not."

We thanked them for their kindness and ambled out into the street. We walked home and went right to bed. We didn't say a word to each other.

CHAPTER 18

The rush and ebb of wind-driven raindrops on the bedroom window did not help me sleep. I thought only of being stranded in Beirut. We were almost out of money, and I was sure that we owed George a ton on top of that. If we couldn't sell the car, we were screwed. I also owed Willard quite a bit from the trip, and he would need to get it from me if we ever made it back to Germany, and if I even would have received some by that time. The whole thing was a house of cards built on tenuous eventualities, not to mention the local scene in Beirut—the biggest unknown of all. We had to get out of here. Fear, disabling fear—night-magnified and real, vivified by our loneliness and vulnerability—stole my sleep.

"Are you asleep?"

"No."

"What are we gonna do?"

"I don't know."

"Do you think George can help us get out of here?"

"I'm sure he's screwed too. He's been spending money like it's going out of style. He was counting on selling his car, just like we were."

"We gotta get outta here."

"No shit."

The rest of the night faded away, slinking between fitful rest and tired fear.

"Wake up, T. It's George."

"Where?"

"Outside."

I saw the familiar figure of George dry shaving outside of our door. I hadn't seen him do that since we were in Ankara. This time, though, he was smoking a cigarette. "Good morning, brudders. How did you sleep?"

"Shitty."

"What do you mean?"

"We met some guys who gave us some bad news."

"Oh?"

"Have you heard about the new tax on used cars?"

"I heard something about it. So what?"

"It's killed the used car market."

"I do not believe that."

"That's what these guys said, and one of them worked for a bank. He said they weren't giving out any more loans on used cars."

"Are you quitting before we even try to sell your car?"

"No, George. We were just surprised to hear about it."

"I know. I was too. I also have much at stake, maybe more than you two. We'll do fine. Must I ask you to trust me again?"

"No, George, you know better than that."

"I know. Look, brudders, I will make sure that you get out of Beirut if I have to buy your plane tickets myself. I can always take your car and sell it. I know I can do that. Does that make you feel any better?"

"Look, George, you've already done too much for us. Let's just see if we can sell our car. Are you going to try and sell yours too?"

"I might wait for now, until the market steadies. It is probably not the best time right now. . . . Let's go to the market."

We showered and dressed then drove both cars to the market. We followed George through a bunch of winding streets to an area by the sea. It was basically a parking lot. The rain had slowed to a light drizzle. There were about ten cars parked with about fifteen sleazy dudes hanging around. Most of the cars were pretty nice: pimpmobiles like George's, Mercedes, a Jag, an older BMW. The VW square back with a bad luggage rack looked out of place. George started talking to a few of the guys. We just hung out by the car. He was gone about half an hour. We didn't get any nibbles while he was gone. Then he walked back.

"What's the story, George?"

"It's not good. What you heard is true. Things have fallen off. Prices are down and no one is even buying."

"Great. What do we do now?"

"We can try for a while. It won't hurt. A less expensive car like yours might sell faster."

"Okay."

We hung around all that day. The most interest that we had was a dog that came up and pissed on a tire.

"I have another question, George. What was that shit about the luggage rack helping to sell the car? I haven't seen one luggage rack the whole time I've been in Beirut. And it's a shitty one too. It doesn't even look like a luggage rack."

"I don't know. This is just what Issa Ahmad said."

Willard and I looked at each other. George looked at us both. It was sort of pitiful how we all looked.

"Oh well. Shit or go blind." It was the most appropriate thing I could utter.

"What does that mean?" George asked.

"Never mind. Let's go back to the White House. I'm hungry."

"Me too."

"I knew you fellas would be all right!" George slapped our backs, got between us, and walked us to our car, arms over our shoulders. "You fellas drive to the hotel. I'm going to talk to these guys a little more. I'll see you back there."

George lit up another cigarette. It was about the third one I'd seen him smoke that day.

"What's with that fucker? I never saw him smoke before. Do you think he's nervous?"

"Aren't you nervous? Of course he's nervous. He's right when he says that he has more at stake than we do, and I'm sure he feels responsible for us too. Let's give him a break."

"Yeah. Let's do something for him for a change. Let's take him out to dinner on the MC."

"Yeah. He'll like that. Let's go back and tell Anna and her mother to get ready. We haven't seen them in a few days anyway."

We drove back to the apartments and parked around back. We used George's spot that he usually parked in. We got out and rode the elevator to the sixth floor. We walked up to his apartment. We heard some voices. It became clear that it was Anna and her mother. They were arguing. I think it was in Italian.

"What do you want to do?"

"I don't know."

"Go ahead and knock."

"No, you."

"Come on, T."

I knocked lightly but they didn't hear. I knocked louder. They stopped yelling. Anna's mother came to the door.

We spoke briefly in German. She was very upset. She answered no to the question of whether we could do anything to help. She also declined our offer to go out to dinner with us. She smiled when we told her that we would pay, and then she laughed when we said that we weren't really going to pay, that we were just going to use our credit card. By this time, Anna had come to the door.

"Hello, Bob. Hello, Bill. Please come in. I am sorry that we were not kind enough to invite you in." She glared at her mother.

"We're sorry to interrupt, but we wanted to invite you out to dinner. Would you like to come? It's on us."

"Thank you, but I don't think so."

"Oh, come on, Anna. You look like you could use some fresh air. We haven't seen you in days. We'll all go out when George gets back."

At this her mother spat an unrecognizable word out of her mouth and left the room.

"Please forgive my mother. She is very upset."

"Is there anything we can do to help, Anna? You know we'd do anything for you."

"I know you would. You are good boys. No, there is nothing you can do. I'll tell George that you want to go to dinner. He won't be long, will he?"

"No, I don't think so." We got up to leave. "We don't want to go so long without seeing you again, Anna. Please take care of yourself."

"I will." She kissed us both on our heads. "Good night."

"Good night, Anna."

We didn't talk until we were in the elevator.

"I wonder what all that was about."

"I don't know but it was plenty ugly."

"I wonder what that fucker is up to."

"You got me. Something, though."

We went back to our apartment and had a few beers. Someone had been in the apartment. I could tell because a pair of boxers had been up against the bedroom door, and they had been pushed aside. The place didn't look any cleaner, though. George walked in about half an hour later. He was drunk, and had a Kent hanging out of his mouth.

"How are you, my brudders?"

"We're fine, George. How are you?"

"Terrible. Wonderful. I'm drunk."

"We can see that. I didn't even know you drank, or smoked for that matter."

"I haven't done either for a while, but now is a good time to start again."

"Is something wrong?"

"Is something wrong. . . . Is something wrong? Not horrible, but yes, something is wrong. The situation with the cars is a problem."

"Yeah, we'll have to see how that works out."

"Yes, we will. I also have another problem. I think Anna is pregnant. She has not had a period for weeks or months."

Willard and I looked at each other.

"Oh, shit. Sorry, George. We know how shitty that can be." I continued, "We went up to your apartment to ask Anna and her mom if they wanted to go out to dinner tonight. They were arguing and both were very upset."

"Yes, I know. Her mother wants to kill me. I haven't been staying there. She wants us to get married. Anna knows better. It is a problem. I have other problems. Beirut is getting to be a problem."

"Let's go out to eat, George. We'll put it on our card. Let us do something for you for a change."

"Okay, my brudders. But don't worry about doing anything for me. You have already done everything."

ROBERT TIBOLT

As usual, things became less clear. We finished our beers and walked out into the Beirut night.

174

CHAPTER 19

The drizzle had stopped, and a low mist now shrouded the buildings of Hamra. We walked slowly, side by side, down the sidewalk, almost oblivious to the steady crowds of people walking to and fro beside us. George was pretty drunk. He was wobbling a little.

"I am getting sick of this bullshit."

"What bullshit, George?"

"Almost all of it. Beirut is a difficult city, and this is a difficult time. Things have not been going well."

"What things do you mean? We still don't have this all figured out, George. Are you doing anything special here, or are you just on vacation, or what?"

"What don't you have figured out? How many times must I tell you? I will tell you anything that I can. Please."

"Why are we here?"

"In Beirut?"

"Yeah. Is it just to have fun?"

"It is more than that, but mostly that. For you it is only for fun. I do not involve you in the business part of my visit."

"What is that, George?"

"It is as I have already told you fellas. I help the PLO. I have a certain amount of influence and popularity that I share with them to help them with their cause."

"You didn't have much of either the other day, George."

We all started laughing.

"Those sons of bitches. It was my own fault, though. I was foolish. Usually, my support takes place in other countries. I am not as well known here. I am involved in something different here. I probably should not say more than that."

"George!" Willard and I stared at him very hard.

"It is better that I not tell you more. It is better for you."

"Are we safe here?"

"You are safe."

"How safe?"

"Safer than in America."

"I doubt that."

"Safer than in Detroit or New York."

"So what? We don't live in those places. There's too much going on here that we don't understand, George. I don't want to be a headline or a statistic."

"What do you mean?"

"'American Students Blown Up in Beirut.'"

"Don't be foolish."

At that moment, at the very instant that the sound of George's statement faded, distant reports of weapons chattered violently. Every person walking on the crowded sidewalk stopped to listen. Quizzical disbelief and sickening anguish filled their faces.

"That sounds like gunfire, George." I had to laugh.

"It is not funny, brudder."

I had never heard automatic gunfire before. I had fired an AR-15 once in a semiautomatic mode. But full automatic fire was different. It was an embodiment of chaos, unpredictable and dangerous, and the quiet that followed was not reassuring. It merely compelled us to listen for the next burst. The listening overtook every other thought and the compulsion to do it lingered like the smoke and the smell of gunfire itself.

"What should we do?"

"Let's eat."

"Besides that."

"Drink heavily."

"Good idea."

We turned into a nice restaurant.

"They will probably raise the prices of things right in front of us because of the gunfire."

"Why is that?"

"It just happens when there is trouble."

There were rumors in the restaurant as to the what and the where and the why, and of course, the who, of the gunplay. It was either the Palestinians, or the Phalangists, or the army, or the Israelis, or the Tigers, or the Shiites, etc. George thought it was either the PLO or the Phalangists.

"It was about time for something to happen."

People were drinking like crazy. We fit right in. We had some food; it was the one meal that I can't recall what we had. We paid our bill and left a good tip for their kind act of not having raised the menu prices on us. After we left, we walked back to the White House amid mild mob-like behavior. People were pretty excited. Shop owners were rolling down garage-door fronts and stretching folding-bar barriers across their stores. Cabs were at a premium. Strangers touched each other and talked like old friends. I saw several women crying. One was quite excited.

"I just know it is going to be like '73. I just know it. I know it."

"What happened in '73?"

"Many people were killed. I lost my brother-in-law. It was senseless and cruel. I will leave here this time. I will not be involved again."

"What's she talking about, George?"

"When the government lost control almost two years ago. The army had many battles with the PLO and hundreds of people died. After that, the Syrians came in and tried to defend the PLO. It was very bad."

"You never told us about this, George." I tried to laugh.

"You are seeing the making of history. You will also see more." He didn't even try to laugh. We walked back to the White House. On the way, we had to go through several checkpoints manned by young men who looked about Willard's and my age. Most of them were quite nice and only wanted to see our ID and ask us where we were going. They were all especially interested in our answer of the White House. George explained everything and dropped a few names like Abu Sultan that seemed to work. We finally made it back to our room. We didn't hear any more gunfire.

"Are you fellas going to bed?"

"We might stay up and drink a few beers. What about you, George?"

"I am very tired. I think I will go to bed."

"Are you staying upstairs?"

"I don't know. I haven't talked to Anna in a couple of days."

"Stop by and see her. Maybe she's had her period."

"I am afraid that even that would not help our relationship. . . . You and I will talk tomorrow. We have some things that we need to talk about. Good night, my friends."

"Good night, George."

I watched George walk out into the night. He stopped and talked to one of the guards of the Research Center, and then Abu Sultan came out. He was acting kind of pissed off at George. I sure couldn't figure any of this out. Willard and I drank our beers and fell asleep listening for more gunfire. If I had cared about anything other than leaving Beirut, I might have been more concerned.

A mild sense of dread preceded my awakening. It was nothing serious and nothing definite. After I awoke, I could still not identify the source of my anxiety. The closest I could come to it was that the old, familiar sense of not belonging, of being in the wrong place, was starting to reappear. In the past I had always been able to listen to that voice and leave. My exits had invariably been characterized by ignominy and supplication, but at least I had escaped with my skin. I felt a new conviction to continue my string of strategic retreat.

"Willard, let's get out of this fucking place. It's not safe here anymore."

"I agree. Let's talk to George."

We got up, showered, and dressed. I organized my things into my traveling bag, and I saw that Willard did the same. When we had finished, we realized that we had no way to find George.

"Let's go upstairs and see Anna. Maybe she can help us figure out what's going on."

This time we climbed the stairs. The stairwell was partly open to the outside. I glanced down and could see the front of the apartment. Getting into a cab were Anna and her mother. The cabbie was loading their bags into the trunk.

"Anna!" I yelled out of the stairwell opening.

She turned and looked up at me, then waved for us to come down.

We hustled down the stairs to the ground floor and ran over to her.

"What are you doing, Anna? Leaving without saying good-bye? What about George?"

"I felt sorry about leaving you two without saying good-bye, but not George. He and I are through. We are going back to Italy."

She began to scribble on a sheet of paper. "I left a note and address with Abu Sultan for you, but here is the address. We would love to have you visit us sometime. Italy is beautiful, and much safer than here."

"Are you flying home?"

"Yes. And you two should do the same thing. There is much that you do not know about Beirut, and about George too. I love him, but I could never live with him. Do not stay long enough to find out how dangerous it is with him."

"You never told me any of this when I asked you, Anna. What's the deal?"

"I couldn't. I still can't. Just take my advice and leave Beirut. It is a good time to leave. Good-bye, Bob. Good-bye, Bill. We must go. Our plane leaves soon. Please do visit us. I mean it. I will miss you both."

Her mother was dabbing a tear from the corner of her eye, and soon we were all crying and hugging and kissing. It was a mess. I hated to see her go. It was more than just her going; it was what it said about George, and now us, for that matter. As the cab pulled away, I began to experience another old emotion: loneliness—the loneliness that I felt when we parted ways in the Turkish desert. I was sure that Willard felt it too.

"Where's George?"

"I seem to recall having asked that question once or twice before."

We walked back into the apartment building and asked for Abu Sultan. We were told he was not there.

"What was that gunfire about last night anyway?"

"I did not hear it."

"Surely you heard about it."

"Yes. I do not know what it was about."

We walked away.

"That guy was a big help. What do you want to do?"

"Let's walk over and get those tapes from that guy. He'll tell us what happened."

We walked down Hamra. Things looked normal enough. We found our way to the record store and walked in.

"Hello, my friends. I was wondering if I would see you again."

Willard and I looked at each other.

"You said that you would return yesterday."

"Oh. Do you have our tapes?"

"Yes, of course. I think that you will enjoy them. Is there anything else I can help you with?"

"Uh, yeah. What was the gunfire about last night?"

"I did not hear it myself, but I understand that it was some random shooting by some PLO commandos. It was not directed at anyone, just some shooting into the air."

"It sure got everyone upset."

"It is very upsetting to hear gunfire in Beirut. One never knows when it will represent a war. We are always merely one incident away from war."

I looked into his eyes. They were red-rimmed, and the upper eyelid on the left was twitching. He blinked a few times. His eyes looked wet as he cleared his throat. This man was in no shape to tell anything but the truth, so I asked him the only question that meant anything to me.

"Is it safe in Beirut?"

"I really do not know. No one knows."

When we found George, he was sitting in the lobby of the White House cutting up an orange with a sharp kitchen knife. He had a cigarette going in an ashtray. Abu Sultan was sitting with him. It was the first time I had seen them together in public for a while. They stood up.

"Hello, George. Hello, Abu Sultan."

We shook hands all around.

"Hello, fellas. Sit down."

"You were right last night, George."

"Oh?"

"We need to talk."

"We will talk."

"Maybe you could bring us up to date on things here."

"In Beirut?"

"Sure, why not?"

"Where shall I begin?"

"How about with last night?"

"Last night . . . the gunfire?"

"Sure."

George took a deep breath. Abu Sultan spoke. "Last night there may have been an attack on one of our camps. There was some suspicious activity beyond the perimeter of Tel al-Zaatar. One of our soldiers fired into the night. We do not think there was any fire returned, nor do we think that anyone was injured. It was unfortunate, but I do not think that any harm was done."

I nodded.

"How are things this morning?"

"Things seem normal."

"But people are very nervous."

"Yes, people are very nervous."

"We are nervous."

George laughed. "Everyone is nervous, Bill." He took another deep breath. "Do you fellas want to leave Beirut?"

"Yes, George."

He nodded his head and rubbed his hand over his chin and cheek.

"We have to get back, George. I have to get back to America, and Bob has to get back to Germany. I can't get back to America unless he comes with me; I need to get some money from him, and he has to be there to get it from the bank. If it ever came."

Willard looked at me.

"We don't feel safe here anymore, George. It's time to go anyway."

"I know, fellas. The situation is a little difficult."

"We don't want to put you in a jam, George. I imagine the thing with the cars is a problem."

"It is a problem, but I am not too worried about it. Let us figure out something that will make you fellas happy. . . . How is your money?"

"Bad. We don't have money to pay you what we owe you, and we don't have money to leave Beirut with."

"As far as the money that you owe me, it is probably about seven hundred dollars. That includes the apartment for a month, the food and beer from the store, and the repair and painting of the car. Okay?"

"Sure. How do things look as far as letting the car be the payment for that?"

"I said that I would do that, and I will. I do not know how that will work out. Maybe I will lose, but maybe I will make some money."

"It's your car, Willard. Is that okay?"

"That's fine. You and I can work it out later."

"Sure."

"Now. About leaving Beirut. When do you want to leave?"

"As soon as possible, George."

"Okay." He rubbed his face again as he tapped the ash off the end of the cigarette. "How can we pay for this?"

Willard began to squirm.

"What's the matter, Willard?"

"I just discovered that my Master Charge expired."

"Willard! You gotta be kidding!"

"I'm not kidding."

George didn't look too happy. "Can you send for money?"

"No, George. I've already spent and charged so much money my father is going to kill me as it is."

"Can you get another Master Charge?"

"I don't know, but it would probably take some time even if I could."

"Yes." George took another deep breath. "If I were to pay for your plane tickets, could you repay me?"

"Yes, but I'm not sure when. I have a thousand dollars waiting for me in Germany, hopefully. I have to pay for Willard's ticket home because he spent the money that he was supposed to use for that on our trip here, and he paid for almost everything. So I have to pay for that. How much are tickets from here to Germany?"

"I am not sure. I don't think it is too much, maybe three hundred each."

"Willard's ticket back to America is going to be about four hundred, so maybe it could work out just about right."

"Will you have enough money to stay in Germany if you send me this money?"

"Not really, but I don't need that much. I already have a place to stay, and I can always get some emergency money from my professor."

"Okay. Why don't you check on plane tickets."

"Sure, George. . . . Say, we're sorry about Anna. We were sorry to see her go."

"It could not be helped. She is a good woman, but it would not work with us. She could not keep up with me."

"Who could, George?"

He looked at me. He tried to smile. It was a feeble effort.

We walked down to the street and used a pay phone.

"When do you wish to travel?"

"As soon as possible."

"I am looking. . . . There is nothing available into Stuttgart for a week. Is that soon enough?"

"What else do you have?"

"I will look. . . . Do you want to go to Berlin?"

"No."

"I am looking."

"Willard, this is looking grim. There's nothing for a week into Stuttgart."

"This could be World War III by then."

"How about Munich?"

"That would be fine."

"I have two seats to Munich on a flight tomorrow."

"Great. We'll take them." I gave the man the necessary information.

"How would you like to pay for these? The fare is two hundred and ninety-seven dollars each."

"Can we go to your office in Beirut?"

"Yes. We will hold these reservations for you today. Go to our office in Ras Beirut. It is two blocks off Hamra. I will give you the address."

We went back to the lobby and George was still sitting there with Abu Sultan.

"George, we got two flights out of here tomorrow."

"Good. How do you pay for it?"

"We need to go to the Lufthansa office here in Ras Beirut today and buy them. They're two hundred and ninety-seven each."

"All right."

George took six of his $100 traveler's checks out and signed them. He gave them to Bill.

"Take these to the money changer across the street. Get dollars—they will accept them at the airline. Tell him you are doing it for me, and he should not charge you for it. Do you know how to get to the office?"

"Yes. The airline guy gave us directions. Thanks, George. You're really something."

"Would you do the same for me?"

"Of course."

"Then it is the same. I have an errand to do myself. I will see you back here later. Then we can go out tonight."

"Okay, George."

He and Abu Sultan left the hotel through a rear entrance to the lobby. We walked out through the main entrance and crossed the street. We exchanged George's traveler's checks and began our walk to the Lufthansa office. Things still looked normal. I began to relax a little.

"I think we might even make it out of this rathole, Willard."

"I'll believe it when I see it."

"Yeah. Me too."

We found the office and completed the transaction without a hitch. We even had our passports.

"Please check in one hour before your departure time of ten thirty-two. This is necessary for international flights. Do you have any questions?"

"No. Well, yes. Has there been any trouble with flights getting out of Beirut?"

"No, sir, what do you mean?"

"It's been business as usual?"

"Well, it has been very busy. People are leaving Beirut."

"Do you overbook?"

"Yes, sometimes."

"Is this flight overbooked?"

"Yes, but not too much."

"Great."

"Your best chance is to check in early."

"Thank you."

The packing went pretty quickly. I already had most of the stuff in the bag. Actually, I emptied everything out and repacked it. Down in the corner I found a little manilla-colored envelope with a "Dr. T" written on it. I hadn't seen it before. After I opened it, I remembered my roommate Norty's words that he had left a surprise for me in the bag. In the envelope were two fat joints.

"Hey, Willard. Look at this."

"Where did you get those?"

"They were in my bag."

"What? We traveled from Germany through all those fucked-up countries with weed? Are you crazy? They put people to death in Turkey for that. You fuckhead!"

"Keep your shirt on. I didn't know it was there. My roommate put them in the bag."

"Did he tell you about it?"

"Yeah, but I didn't really think about it."

"I can't believe you did that to us."

"Look, if it bothers you that much, I'll throw them away." I started to walk to the bathroom.

"Wait a minute. Don't be stupid. Fire one up."

"In here?"

"Let's go out on the stairs."

"Okay."

I took one of the numbers and found some matches. We went out on the stairs and walked up halfway between two floors, sat down, and lit it. It was a little harsh, but it seemed to work okay.

"What are you going to remember most about this trip?"

"George."

"Me too."

"That crazy little fucker. I wonder if we'll ever find out what he's up to."

"I doubt it. I wonder if even he knows what he's involved in."

"Oh, yeah. George is too slick to get conned. As my Uncle Joe used to say, 'You can't shit a shitter.'"

"I don't know. George hangs around with some pretty rough customers. Do you remember those guys at the Istanbul Hilton? They looked like the mob."

"Yeah."

"What do you think got Anna upset enough to leave?"

"I don't know. Maybe George will tell us tonight."

As we got high, my fear evaporated. We really got a buzz. I looked out over the lot in front of the White House. I saw three different guards on patrol. They kept walking a beat around the perimeter. The farthest they got was about one hundred yards away from the Research Center. At that point, they peeked down the alley where Willard and I had hidden from the cabbie, then turned back.

"Hey, look at that guard snooping down the alley, Willard. He must remember us hiding there like rats."

"Another time you almost got us killed."

"What do you mean? I thought that guy was going to pull out a heater on us. Anyway, I didn't see you grab him and throw him to the ground."

"He was too old. It wouldn't have been fair; it would have been like striking out the pitcher."

We began to laugh nonstop for about five minutes. We were pretty relieved to be leaving Beirut. It was a great place; it really was. It was the best place I had ever been, bar none. But enough was enough. It was getting too crazy, and our position was too fragile. No money. George was starting to lose it, smoking and drinking, and he was probably out of money too. His girlfriend, who loved his ass, had left him. Things were getting strange here politically, and it looked like something bad could happen. Getting back to Germany would seem like getting back home.

"Let's find that little fucker!"

"Yeah. Hey, Willard, do you think you can squeeze one more night out of that Master Charge?"

"I don't see why not. What are they going to do, take it? Let 'em."

We walked down to the lobby and looked around. The boy at the desk hadn't seen George.

"Let's walk around. It may be our last chance."

CHAPTER 20

We tried to find George on our last afternoon in Beirut, but we couldn't. So we went out drinking and ended up at our favorite watering hole. There we ran into Abu Sultan. He seemed to be looking for us. He started buying us drinks, but I noticed that he wasn't drinking anything himself. So I started to drink water. He started to tell us more about George and what he was doing in Beirut. George was helping the PLO by acting as a go-between. He wouldn't exactly say between whom. It was very complicated and very important, he said. He did not want to go into too much detail, for the good of George and for our own good. I looked at Willard and shook my head. He said the reason he was telling us anything at all was for our own safety. It would be very unlikely that we would get involved in any of this, but, if we did, we needed to know what to say. I reminded him that we would be leaving the next day. He said he knew that. I asked him if he was sure he wanted to tell us anything, because right now we didn't know anything and didn't want to know anything. He said he only needed to get a couple of things straight. One was that he wanted us to say that we traveled together the whole time with George, and that we didn't separate when George went to Cyprus. As a matter of fact, he wanted us to forget that George had gone to Cyprus. The other was to avoid any kind of suspicious behavior until we left; he wanted us to stay with him the whole time. He said that he would get us to the airport. He said that things were heating up in Beirut now, and sometimes it was difficult getting across the city or getting out of the airport. I was pretty sobered up with all of his talk, so I had another drink. Abu Sultan closed the discussion by saying that if we ever got into a jam with the PLO, to use his name or that of Ahmed Rahmeh, an officer whose name was widely recognized, and whom we had met the day that we had spent at the PLO camps; he was the last guy who talked to us. Abu Sultan also asked us not to say anything to George about our discussion.

We went back to the White House. We found George waiting for us in the lobby. He was really glad to see us. He apologized for all the trouble we had experienced. We said that we had had nothing but fun, and that there had been no trouble. George wanted to take us out for a great last night in Beirut. We told him that we wanted to take him out. So we both decided to take out each other.

The last night was memorable. We ate, drank, danced, watched belly dancers, smoked hash, gambled at the Holiday Inn, and rolled in about four in the morning. I felt it was a fitting end to the trip. We got back to the room. Our bags were all packed and lined up. Our flight left at 10:30 a.m. We said good night to Abu Sultan, and he said he would pick us up at 8:00 a.m. We crashed hard.

George woke us up, I guessed for the last time. He had brought us some fruit and bread and coffee. We chowed down between showers. He helped us carry our bags down. Willard gave him the keys to the VW. What papers we had were in the glove box. George told us that he was taking our car to a place to try to sell it, otherwise he would have gone to the airport with us. We understood and thanked him for everything. We told him that if we found any more papers on the car in Germany, we would send them. He told us he would try to visit us in the USA. We all said that we hoped we would see each other again. I hoped George would make it out of there in one piece. We said good-bye. It was pretty powerful stuff. At the end, I couldn't look at him; I was crying like a baby. He grabbed me around the neck and kissed me. I kissed him back. Abu Sultan rounded us up into the car, and we left. Even the guards at the Research Center were touched.

Abu Sultan was a normal driver, not like George or Bill. We didn't say much. I asked him why he didn't want us to have mentioned anything to George about what he had told us. He told us that George had plenty on his mind and had expressly forbade Abu Sultan from saying anything about anything to us. He didn't want to expose us to any more risk than we were already in. When I asked how much that was, all he said was not much.

It was quite a long drive to the airport. The last part was a stretch out in the open. As we approached it, we saw a line of cars stopped in front of us. There were a few police cars at the front of the line, but nothing in front of them. Everyone was in their cars except the police, who were crouched down behind theirs. Abu Sultan became very upset; he said it was the only thing he had been afraid of. We stopped our car behind the last one in line and shut the motor off. Then we could hear the gunfire erupting not too far away. It was that damned automatic fire again and lots of it. Abu Sultan stuck his head out and conversed by shouting in Arabic with several other motorists. He told us that the road was closed, and that there were no prospects of its being reopened anytime soon. *Here we go again,* I thought. We talked about our options. It seemed that there was really no other way to get to the airport. We were screwed. Back to Beirut.

On the way back, Abu Sultan was visibly upset. He started to explain why this was a bad situation. He said that George was involved in something very important, complicated, and dangerous. He also said that we were involved, much more involved than we could imagine. He said that it wouldn't be safe for us to go back to the White House. When we asked him where it would be safe for us to go, he said he didn't know, maybe the American embassy. Then he said that we could drive by the White House and see what was going on. I didn't like the way he said it, but I didn't have any other ideas.

We drove by the lot next to the Research Center and the White House. We approached the same way that we had the very first day that we had arrived in Beirut, by the alley where we had almost gotten ourselves killed.

I said to Willard, "Hey look, there's your car." It was parked in that same alley, facing across the lot to the Research Center. On the roof of it, though, there was a crate. It was sitting in that luggage rack that George's buddy had installed.

What the hell is that, I wondered. Just then, there was an explosion of sound and smoke. I had flown model rockets as a kid. When they take off there is a pressured *whoosh*. The fiercest series of *whooshes* I had ever felt or heard tore the crate off the roof of the car amid a whirlpool of thick, swirling, white smoke. Immediately, there came a corresponding series of explosions across the lot. I could tell it was the Research Center that had been hit. I felt the shock wave from the explosions with the tearing, crunching blast. I didn't see any people. I instinctively looked for the guards on patrol, but there were none. Abu Sultan slammed the car into reverse, did one of those power slides into forward, and hauled ass out of there.

Willard and I simultaneously erupted. We were all over Abu Sultan, screaming and yelling, almost crying. He was driving like a madman. He told us to keep quiet and that he was taking us to a safe place. I said that the only place that I would feel safe would be Germany. He laughed. He kept motoring through a bunch of old neighborhoods until we arrived at a familiar place. It was the last PLO building where we had been detained. Abu Sultan pulled up slowly to the back. He told us to wait in the car. He walked up to the back door. They had their own guards on patrol. They knew Abu Sultan and waved him in. Then a couple of guys with guns came to the car and grabbed our bags. We followed them in. We walked through the communications room and back into the office of Ahmed Rahmeh. He was sitting there. He almost looked like he was expecting us. Abu Sultan sat quietly in the back of the room.

"We meet again."

"Could someone tell us what in the hell is going on?"

"It is complicated."

"That much we know."

"I will tell you what I can. In truth, you do not want to know any more than I relate."

"I'm sure of that. Where's George?"

"George is gone."

I turned and looked at Abu Sultan. He was stern-faced and staring out the window.

"Gone?"

"He is in a safe place."

"I'm glad he's safe."

"You are as well."

"We don't feel safe."

"You will be safe as long as you do what I tell you."

"We have little choice."

"You are correct in that. . . . You see, there was a plan. The plan was carried out. It was, however, complicated by a breakdown in our security.

Some lower-level soldiers learned of the plan and intervened. That, in fact, is why you were prevented from reaching the airport. The battle was staged to prevent your leaving."

He stopped talking. I knew why he stopped. The news was too much for us to comprehend. My brain swam in little shimmery lights for a few seconds; I almost passed out. I knew that Willard was dying too. Ahmed Rahmeh continued.

"It was better for you that you did not arrive there. There you would have been confronted by some of our soldiers who do not know the entire plan, and the result would have been unpredictable. Now that you are here, we are again in control of the situation. We will arrange for your leaving Beirut. I will do everything that I can to conduct you safely back to Germany. As you might guess, this is a hectic time. There are many things that need to be done. Please be patient."

I started to laugh. Then I stopped. In walked George. He was apparently not expected. The room instantly turned into a clusterfuck. Willard and I looked at each other as three grown men screamed at each other in several Middle Eastern languages. A couple of guards edged their way headfirst through the door before Ahmed slammed it in their faces. It seemed that Abu Sultan and Ahmed were very mad at George, and he was equally bullshit with them. I interrupted.

"Hi, George."

"Hello, Bill."

"Is there a chance that someone can explain some of this to us?"

"Of course," Ahmed interjected, "we will do that. Until this moment"—he glowered at George—"George has been a loyal and helpful friend of the PLO. He became involved in a very important plan. You fellows were also involved. But things became complicated, as I have told you.

"It is difficult to explain everything. The whole story is too complicated and goes back too far, as far back as the Palestinian problem. But I will summarize the relevant parts for you." Ahmed sighed deeply.

"George will have to tell you his part, but, as for the PLO, your story began on the day that you saw Arafat in Damascus. Do you remember that day? We took pictures of the crowd, a routine procedure, and when we reviewed them, we noticed you two. It was very obvious that you were out of place; especially you, Bob. We saved your pictures and circulated them among our people. Imagine our surprise when you appeared in Beirut in the company of George. We did not know what to think. Coincidences do not exist. You were both very lucky that we did not understand things more clearly, or we would have taken definitive measures immediately."

Through all of this, George had said nothing to us. He sat with a dour look on his face, not looking at either Bill or me.

"George had been on a mission for us. He was to bring some important supplies to Beirut. It is better that we not discuss the exact nature of these items. In any case, these items were brought in and used as planned."

Still George didn't say anything. He was looking now like he was going to explode.

"Now the question is, how do we get you fellows back to Germany? It is not an easy task. First, Beirut is on alert, and the airport is heavily guarded. I would not be surprised if some flights have been cancelled. Second, there are elements within our own organization who believe that you two are CIA agents involved in the rocket attack on our Research Center. We do not have the means to inform these people of the truth. Now that there is an emergency, each unit is following prearranged plans. We must prevent your detection. I suggest you leave immediately with Abu Sultan. He will take you to a safe place where you can wait for nightfall. Then we will escort you to the American embassy. If worse comes to worst, they can use their submarine exit to get you out of Beirut."

This was all too much to take. Apparently, also for George.

"They will come with me."

"Do not be foolish, George. You can do nothing for them. You are also regarded as an enemy now, as you know. What good would it do for you all to be killed together? Please be reasonable."

He looked very hard at George. I could tell by the way that George's bad eye was looking around that he was searching for something, a way out or an answer to a question. It made me very suspicious of Ahmed.

"Some things are worse than death."

It was probably a true statement, but I sure didn't like it applied to anything having to do with me. Ahmed uttered a harsh-as-death invective at George, and pointed at us as he said it, waving a raft of papers with his hand. I had to ask.

"What are those?"

"It is a CIA information sheet that they give to their agents before an assignment. It is one about Lebanon. It could easily have been found in your bags. Look."

I read it. It began innocently enough:

Mount Lebanon, 3000 m, separated from Anti-Lebanon mountain range by Biqa' (Bekaa) Valley. Anti-Lebanon, 2700 m, continues south to the Hermon range. Biqa' Valley 900 m; Orontes flowing north and the Litani flowing south arise in Biqa'. Springs on Mount Lebanon make it possible to cultivate crops at 1500 m with terracing: bananas on the coast; olives, vines, and figs on low foothills; cereals, apricots, and pears on the middle slopes; and apples and potatoes on the higher levels.

Highly urbanized: 61% live in urban centers with
pop >5000. Percentages of groups living in cities: 84% of
Sunnites, 60% of Greek Orthodox, 45% of Maronites, 55% of
Shiites, and 55% of Druses. 1295/mi², second only to Bahrain
among Arab states.
Climate. Remnants of the past. Myths. Cultural history.
Political history. Government. Military. Customs. Drug
culture. PLO camps, including PLO Research Center.

The information about the Research Center was underlined. I guess
in the wrong hands it could be damning evidence of our complicity
with the CIA.

"Are you threatening to use this against Bill and me?"

"I am merely using whatever means at my disposal to help George
do the thing that he must do to protect himself and you."

"All right. Bob and Bill can go with Abu Sultan. But I must go also."

"That is impossible. Do not force me to be unpleasant, George. I
will not negotiate with you, my brother."

"Where are you going to take them?"

"Ashrafiya."

"Why would you take them there?"

"It is the last place that anyone would look for them."

"Take me then also."

"Don't be foolish."

I wondered where the place was, and who it was that would look
for us there last. I was afraid I would learn answers to both questions.
George had stopped resisting but whispered to me on the way out
that he would see us in a little while. I didn't know what to think, but
my sense was to trust George. We were herded into a waiting car in a
manner totally reminiscent of our previous escorted tour of Beirut's
PLO bases. I was even more scared this time. I rode shotgun, Willard

and Abu Sultan rode in the back, and some other soldier drove. We rode quietly. I didn't recognize any of the streets that we drove. We finally pulled in front of an apartment building; it was not nearly as nice as the White House. It was older, grey, and absolutely crawling with kids. We picked our way through the urchins and were led into a foyer. There we saw a group of rather rough-looking men. The soldier talked to them in Arabic, and then Abu Sultan chimed in, but in French. He pointed over to us as he spoke, and the men in the group raised their eyebrows as they turned their heads to look at us. We didn't belong here at all. It was grossly absurd—utterly ridiculous—that we were here. I felt that something bad was going to happen.

"Willard, do you remember the cab driver trick?"

"Sure do."

"I think it's about time to pull it again."

"These guys aren't old geezers, we don't know where we are, and there are people already looking for us."

"Yeah, but if we stay here, we're going to really take it up the ass." The feeling of impending doom grew as the conversation between our friends heated up. The local group was vehemently negating everything that the PLO soldier and Abu Sultan were saying. They were gesturing toward us violently and shaking their heads and arms, screaming no with every gesture and word. Abu Sultan calmly spoke on and gestured toward us; we were obviously the topic of conversation. Then I realized that it was just another negotiation, exactly like the haggling we had seen at all the markets. It was getting close to the point where somebody was ready to walk away from the deal. I sensed that Abu Sultan was going to do the walking.

"Willard, somebody's telling lies about us, and I think it's Abu Sultan. Let's get the fuck out of here."

"Okay. On three. One . . . two . . ."

Abu Sultan broke away from the group and his soldier followed. He walked toward us and barked, "Come," as he stomped by. We followed him out. I looked back and the men were still standing in the same spot.

"What the hell were you telling them about us? I know it was a lie. There's nothing true about us that they would be interested in."

"That is where you are wrong. There are many things that are true about you that they were very interested in; the only thing is, you do not know these things about yourselves." We kept walking to the car.

"This is starting to piss me off. The only things that we don't know about ourselves are things that you and George did to us. Stop feeding us all this shit! What's going on?"

Abu Sultan stopped and wheeled into my face. "You smuggled the rocket ignitors into Beirut for George in your fur coats. Do you understand? They were used in the attack on the Research Center that we witnessed. The men that we just left are Phalangists. We set up this meeting to get at one of their leaders, the short man with the beard. He will not leave that building alive. If you are smart, you will get in the car. Otherwise, you will also die."

"You motherfuckers! You crazy motherfuckers!"

Just then I recognized one of the guards from the Research Center standing by the front door of the apartments. I could tell that he had his machine gun under his coat.

"Tell me, Sultan, what were you negotiating with them, or trying to negotiate?"

"I will tell you later."

"You'll tell us now. We're not going anywhere."

"Stay if you wish. You'll be dead in thirty seconds." Then he stopped. "I tried to return you two to the Phalangists. I told them that you two were the CIA agents who arranged the attack on the Research Center, and that they should take you back, for they had worked with you on the attack. I told them that I wanted two of our soldiers whom they had kidnapped in exchange for you two. They of course did not agree, for they had no hand in the Research Center attack. It did bring out Josef Abi Assi, who will be dead on my signal. Now get in the car."

I looked at Willard. He looked at me.

"Three!"

We both ran. I didn't know how he did it with his bum knee, but Willard was ahead of me. I screamed back toward the lobby.

"Get out! They're going to kill you!"

The Research Center guard broke out his weapon and walked into the lobby. There were other soldiers entering the building all the way around it. I didn't see what Abu Sultan did, but I guessed he started firing his weapon. The place turned into a battlefield. We ducked around a corner and kept on running. I looked back and didn't see anybody following us. We kept running up and down side streets until we finally reached a main drag. We stopped and began to walk as calmly as we could. It was then that we saw a remarkable sight: a fire-engine red, gangster whitewalled, '75 Grand Prix doing about a hundred down the street. The crazy little fucker was coming for us.

We started waving our arms like we were Gilligan and the captain seeing a search plane for the first time. I didn't know if George would see us, but he did. He put on the binders and came sliding up to us in a shower of dust and flying gravel.

"Get in!"

"No shit! You really did it this time, George! Give us one good reason why we shouldn't kill your fucking ass right now!"

"Never mind. We have to save our lives. You can kill me later."

He raced off. We were looking around for any trailers. I couldn't see any.

"Slow down, George. There's nobody following us. You're just going to draw more attention to us. Why did you get this fucking pimpmobile anyway?"

"I have to figure out what to do. Do you have your passports?"

"Yes, for once. Them and our plane tickets and nothing else."

"We have to go somewhere safe."

"How about the US embassy?"

"Yeah. We can try. But they may be watching there. I'm sure that they will figure we will try that first. Maybe we should go somewhere else first. I'm not sure."

"Come on, George! Don't get sloppy on us now. This is for all the marbles."

"I am thinking."

His bad eye was really searching; I could tell that he was trying hard. As mad as I was with him, I still loved the bastard. There was nobody else like George.

"How in the fuck could you have done what you did to us? I can't believe it. You just used and abused us. And that buddy of yours, Abu Sultan, would have killed us for nothing. Do you know what he tried to do with us?"

"No, but I can guess."

"He used us as bait to get at Josef Assi. I'm sure the fucker's dead right now. We had to run away from the ambush. We tried to warn him. They thought we were CIA guys who arranged the Research Center attack. How could you have done this to us?"

"We will talk later about this. Now we have work to do. We have to get you out of Beirut."

"Oh no, you're not leaving us this time. When we go, we all go. You're not running out on us again."

"Sure . . . I think I know where to go."

"Where?"

"As he said, the last place that they would look for us." He pulled a U-ey and headed back where we had come from.

"Where the hell are you going, George?"

He turned his head, looked at both of us each with one eye, and smiled.

"Trust me."

We laughed like the marines at Khe Sanh the night before they all died.

"Where are we going?"

"The Saint George Hospital. It is in Ashrafiya."

"You're nuts. What are we going to do at a hospital?"

"You guys are doctors. We're going to hide out."

"We're not doctors, George. We're premeds. We don't know shit."

"You better know something."

We drove around to the back of the hospital and parked behind a trash compacter. We all got out and walked into an employee's entrance. The first thing that we ran into was a rack of white coats. We each put one on and walked to the cafeteria. No one batted an eyelash at us. We grabbed some coffee and sat down.

"Now what, George? I'm not sure what this is doing for us."

"At least it will buy us some time. We have to think of a way to get you guys out of here."

"Would you please, and I mean once and for all, tell us what the hell is going on? Abu Sultan told us that you had us smuggle the ignitors for the rockets into Beirut. Is that true, George?"

Willard and I both stared at him.

"It is true."

"That's a hell of a thing to do to a friend, George. Didn't you care that you put us in danger?"

"I knew that you fellas would make it. There was no question about it. Also, I had no choice. It was a very important thing that you did."

"What, help to blow up your own library? Come on, George!"

"It is more complicated than that. Trouble has been building in Beirut for a long time, and fighting was inevitable. The PLO was suffering at the hands of the Phalangists and was about to lose the ability to stay in Lebanon. We were being squeezed out politically. Israel was behind it; they were supporting the Phalangists. We had to do something."

"Why did you have to blow up your own place? That doesn't make sense."

"We needed an excuse to start a war against the Phalangists. We needed to take control of Beirut or lose everything. We have no place left to go. Israel has eliminated every other natural homeland for us and was trying to finish us off. So I went to Cyprus to talk to them."

"To who? The Israelis? Why would you want to talk to them?"

"They paid me to blow up the Research Center."

"George! You're really fucking crazy. What the hell are you talking about?"

"The Israelis paid me to blow up the Research Center. They figured an intelligence center was there, or so they said, and wanted it destroyed. I was also following orders from within the PLO to attack the Research Center. I took the money for myself, as a small token for my efforts. But I couldn't smuggle the rocket parts in myself. I was too hot. I worked for both sides, and I did not know who would check on me."

"What about us? We traveled with you for over three weeks. Didn't you think anybody noticed that?"

"Sure, but you are innocent. Besides, you fellas have all the luck. Nothing could stop you. You didn't know about it, and you played it cool the whole time."

"You're telling me that the PLO and Israel both wanted to blow up the Research Center. Is that right?"

"That is right."

"No wonder you fuckers can't get along. You're all crazy. You deserve each other."

"Perhaps."

The cafeteria crowd began to thin. It was midafternoon. We had nowhere to go and no plan. We sat quietly and drank our coffee. George finally spoke.

"Here is the problem. We are all three wanted by both sides, all sides if you count the Israelis. I am sure that they would prefer that I was eliminated. So, what can we do?"

"Look, the Americans don't want us. They know that we're not CIA. Do they want you for anything?"

"No, I do not think so."

"So, let's figure out a way to get some American protection. We're American citizens, and you drive an American car. That's gotta be good for something."

George laughed again. Then he stopped. "One of you fellas call the embassy."

"What are we going to say?"

"Find out what they want American citizens to do."

Willard left the table and went to find a pay phone.

"Let's look at the options. What are the ways to get out of the country?"

"We could drive out, but we could only go to Syria, and I know that border is closed. We could fly out, but the airport is too dangerous. We could get on a ferry to Italy. Now that's a chance. I could even take my car. What do you think?"

"Sounds okay. Could we get on one?"

"Maybe."

"It sounds like our best chance."

"Yes, I agree."

"Here's Willard."

"Why do you call him Willard? His name is Bob."

"His name is Bill, George, and Willard is the name of a rat. Get it?"

"Sure. What did they say, Bill?"

"Why did you call me Bill now, George?"

"Never mind! What did they say?"

"They said to leave Beirut."

"Yeah, we knew that."

"How?"

"They suggested flying. I told them that we were being harassed by some of the PLO, and that we did not feel safe going to the airport. The guy said we could come to the embassy, and that they would escort us to the airport."

We looked at each other and nodded.

"What do you think, George?"

"I don't think that they could protect us. They are not aware of the problem. But maybe it could work. Let's go over there."

We finished our fifth cups of coffee and left the cafeteria. On our way out, we dumped our white coats in the laundry, all except Willard, who saved his. It had "X-RAY" stitched above the left breast pocket. He rolled it into a ball and stuck it under his arm. I thought it would be a good nickname for him someday. The back lot looked clear, and we walked to the car. I climbed in back, we drove away, and made time across town to the embassy.

"Okay, what's the plan?"

"I am afraid that the embassy will be under surveillance. My car is too well known to our enemies. I think I will have to drop you fellas off before we get there. I will park it and come after a few minutes."

"No you don't, George! When we said we're leaving together, we meant it. If you have to park the car and walk to the embassy, then we'll do it all together. *Comprende?*"

"Sure."

"Good."

We sat quietly as we approached the road that ran along the water. The embassy was only about a mile away now. I was looking out the back window. I didn't see anything suspicious. George was driving pretty leisurely. I felt the eye working, though, so I was on my toes. I just couldn't figure out what he was up to.

"Hey. I have to check something. Let me see your passports."

"What for?"

"Please give them to me. You will need a visa stamp to get out of the country. I want to see if you have it."

I took out the passport and flipped to the back section.

"Yeah, here it is."

"Yes, but I need to see if it is the right one. There are several different ones, you know. Let me see them."

I gave my passport to Bill.

"Open them up to the visas so I can see them."

Bill handed them over.

"Let me see." George looked at the visas, drove, and kept a lookout all around us. I still didn't know how he could do all that with basically one eye.

"Whaddya think, George?"

"I think . . ."

"What?"

"I think I need to change some money."

We had entered an area with several money changers on the sidewalk. He slowly pulled up next to one and rolled down the window. Then he chattered something, holding out some money and our passports. The money changer took them and walked back to his stall.

"George, what are you doing?"

"They need passports to change money."

"They never did before."

"It is a new law."

"You lyin' sack of shit."

Then he pulled away.

"George!" we screamed as one.

"Now listen, fellas. There is no time. Someone is following us."

I looked back. Sure enough, there was a taxi with four guys in it about fifty yards back. It was some bad boys.

"I will drop you off and you will walk to the embassy. Pick up your passports from the money changer first. Once you are at the embassy, explain the situation. Try to keep me out of it. Just tell them that you made the PLO angry at you by making love to one of their sisters. When you get back to Germany, call me at the White House and tell me where I can reach you."

He pulled around a corner and punched it, first through two alleys and then the wrong way down a one-way street. He lost the trailer cold. We ended up behind a warehouse. We didn't see anybody.

"I am sorry, my brudders, but you will be okay. So will I. But this is it. I love you both."

"George!"

"Every second you waste makes it worse for us all. Good-bye. We will see each other again."

We climbed out. George took off. I have to tell you that it was the last time we saw the bastard.

Willard and I ducked behind a dumpster and waited a few minutes. Then we saw the guys in the taxi. They were driving slowly, all looking and craning around like a four-headed Hydra. Suddenly they stopped, slammed it into reverse, and peeled out. I guessed they had seen George. We got up and started walking to the money changer.

We got there in about five minutes. The man handed the passports over. He gave us walking directions to the embassy. We were about fifteen minutes away.

"Well, Willard, here we are. Again."

"Yeah. You know, I think we're going to be okay. I'm just real worried about George."

"I am too."

"I think the embassy will be able to get us out, don't you?"

"I suppose."

"Maybe we don't need them."

"What are you talking about, T?"

"Follow me." I had seen a sign for a barber. We walked in. "We need shaves and haircuts."

"Of course, gentlemen. Have a seat."

"And we're in a hurry."

"Very good. I will get my brother."

"Also, do you accept Master Charge?"

"No, but the shop next door does. We can arrange it. May I have your card?"

Willard gave it to him.

"It's not worth anything anyway," he whispered to me.

Within a minute, we were getting shaves and haircuts. Willard and I both have tough beards. The guys were having a terrible time. They were cutting us left and right. I remembered a Superman comic issue where one of his enemies was this guy who had been transformed from a gorilla, and he went to get a shave and a haircut. The barber had the little thought balloon drawn in and was thinking, "Gee, this guy must be part gorilla." I looked up at my barber and could almost see him thinking that.

"Just a little bit of a trim on the hair. We don't want to look too good."

"Yes, sir."

They finished. Their styptic pencils really got a workout. They burned us to bits.

"We are sorry that it was so difficult."

"Oh no, it's not your fault. We know we have tough beards. Thank you very much."

Willard wrote in a big tip to the MC slip.

"Now what?"

"Let's just get the fuck out of here. Screw the embassy. I've never known the government to be helpful with anything anyway. Whaddya think?"

"Yeah, let's just go. Let's get a cab. Maybe we can get our first taxi buddy again."

"Yeah." We laughed pretty hard. Willard flagged one down.

"We need to go to the airport. Is the road open?"

"Yes, I believe so."

"Do you accept Master Charge?"

"No, but we can stop at my brother's. He is a money changer. He will do it for us."

"I bet he will." We looked at each other. We didn't even have to laugh. The guy made good time to his brother's, and we got a fistful of money from him. Nobody cared that the card was expired. They probably knew something that we didn't. We drove a ways and made it to the airport road.

"Son of a bitch, it looks open."

"Yes, I think so."

We made it all the way to the entrance of the airport without a problem. There we saw a checkpoint. It was manned by soldiers or police, somebody official looking, in uniform.

"What is this?"

"Nothing. They may ask for your tickets and passports."

We got in line and in about five minutes we pulled up to the gate.

"Are you leaving Beirut?"

"Yes."

"For where?"

"Germany."

"Are you Germans?"

"No, Americans."

He nodded.

"May I see your passports and tickets, please?"

"Yes, of course."

He looked everything over.

"You have several problems."

"Oh?"

"For one thing, you have missed your flights. For another, whose pictures are in these passports?"

"They belong to us."

I thought I saw him wink to the cab driver.

"We just got haircuts and shaves. Our fathers are going to meet us in Germany, and they would have killed us if we showed up looking like we did."

"You are not supposed to change your appearance from your passport picture. It is okay with me, but you may run into trouble at customs."

"Oh well, I think we can work it out."

"I am sure you can. Have a good flight."

"Thank you."

We pulled through the gate.

"That was easy. So far."

"Yeah. . . . Look," I turned to the cabbie, "we're trying to surprise some friends at the airport. Drive real slow past the front entrance once and don't stop. After that, we'll have you go back around and drop us off at Lufthansa. Got it?"

"Yes, of course."

He followed the instructions, and we cruised the front lanes. There was nothing unusual looking, no PLO types hanging around with submachine guns under their coats holding our pictures in their hands.

"Okay. Take it around and drop us off."

He pulled around and then stopped in front of the Lufthansa sign. We looked up and down the sidewalk. It was clear. Willard paid the cabbie, including a handsome tip. We got out. There was a skycap of sorts who asked us if we had any luggage.

"No, but we could use a wheelchair." Willard turned to me, "My knee is killing me, and maybe it could help us look less suspicious."

"Yeah, okay."

He gave us a wheelchair and I pushed Willard through the doors, toward the ticket counter. Just then I saw a guard from the first PLO camp that we had visited. He was the one who led us into the building the very first time that we had tried to go see their camp. He was wandering the lobby of the terminal randomly.

"Willard, don't look now, but we have company. Let's get to that Lufthansa counter and get the hell out of here."

I heard some German being spoken and looked behind us from where it came. It was a group of Germans, tourists for sure, getting out of a bus. I backed us out of the doors and parked Willard next to their bags that were being stacked up on the sidewalk.

"I think it's time to start speaking German again, *gell?*"

"Ja."

We started talking to the people who were milling about after unloading. They were a travel club from Munich and were going home early. They were pretty upset and anxious to get home. We learned that they were heading home for Munich on a flight that was to leave in about two hours. We told them that we were going on that flight, too, and asked if we could walk in with them. They said sure. When all the luggage had been unloaded and reloaded onto carts, we all moved into the lobby together, speaking German, of course. As far as tourists go, Germans are pretty loud and obnoxious, so it seemed that there would be no mistaking us as Germans. The group was about twelve people. A few of them were drunk and really loud. We chimed right in with lots of German. We commanded only the usual looks from other people in the lobby, and I noticed that the PLO guard didn't look at us as we passed.

The reason the Germans were leaving was that there had been a busload of Palestinians ambushed earlier in the day, and something like twenty of them had been killed. The German embassy had ordered all German citizens out of the country. When we told them that we didn't have reservations on the flight, they were pretty skeptical of our chances of getting on. They said that every German would be trying to get out of the country today. They were pretty nice. They let us go ahead of them in line at the ticket counter.

"Darf ich Ihnen helfen?"

"Ja, bitte. Wir möchten nach München fahren."

"Haben Sie Karten?"

"Ja. Dürfen wir Englisch reden, bitte?"

"Natürlich. How may I help you?"

"Like everyone else, we need to leave Beirut."

"Your tickets have expired. You have missed your flight."

"It was unavoidable." I looked at Willard; it was no lie.

"This will be difficult. The flight is full, in fact it is overbooked. I will try to get you on the next available flight."

"Miss, we have a problem. We are at the center of a very dangerous situation, and we need to get out of Beirut now. We need to be on that flight to Munich."

"It is impossible. The soonest that you could travel will be tomorrow, but even that will be difficult. All of those flights are also full."

"All the more reason to get us on this flight. Look, we are American students who got mixed up with the PLO. They are after us. We have to go, or it could mean our lives. I am not kidding."

"You are American? Your German is quite good."

"Thanks. Now, what do you think? Is there any way we can travel today?"

"I do not think so. But I will try. Let me keep your tickets, stand over there, and I will try to get you on as standby. That is the best that I can do. Do you have any luggage?"

"No."

She made a face full of sympathy and disbelief. "Also. What happened to your faces?"

"It's a long story. Just like everything else."

It looked grim for us. There were literally hundreds of people in line at that counter, and all of them were obnoxious Germans. I parked Willard's wheelchair and sat down next to him on the floor. He started to get out to go to the bathroom, but I stopped him.

"Don't walk around. That would look funny. Wheel yourself over there if you have to go."

"Yeah, right."

The time crawled by. I checked in a couple of times with Brigitta. She was nice, but not too optimistic. Then they made a boarding announcement for all people on the flight to go through customs. We wanted to go there, but Brigitta said that we needed a boarding pass, and that she couldn't give us one yet.

"Brigitta. Bri-gitt-aaa. You don't understand. Bill and I could be dead tomorrow if we don't fly out now. I've seen at least one guy in the airport looking for us. We have to fly now. Please."

"I will tell you a secret. There are not nearly enough seats for everyone who wants to fly. There are going to be almost one hundred people who do not get to take this flight. I do have a couple of seats that I can get for you. Your story is the best one that I have heard today, and I will give them to you. When the time comes, you have to do exactly as I say. There will be no second chance. You see, I am also taking the flight. We are evacuating our personnel, and all of these agents go now. You both come with me when I say so. There are going to be some very angry Germans, and I do not want to be here when it happens. *Scheiße Mensch!*"

"Thank you. Thank you. When we get to Germany, we will do anything you want."

She laughed. "Now let me finish."

We stood nearby, and then she started to call out names. Each one she called had to fight his or her way through an unyielding mob to the counter. Most of them were parents with small children. I realized that our story had put us in pretty good company. Brigitta then looked over at us and winked. She said my name and Bill's name over her little intercom system. We, of course, realized that we had made a big mistake in allowing her to do that. I grabbed Willard's wheelchair handles and shoved him through a group of three fat, drunken men, excusing myself in German as I did it. I looked behind me once and saw some PLO soldier types trying to fight their way through the mob. They were having a tough time because the mob was starting to close in on the counter. Brigitta and her other pals were right behind us. Behind them, the airport police had formed a human wall. They pushed back the mass of Teutonic anger and slammed some steel doors behind us.

I stopped and gave Brigitta a big hug. Willard got out of the wheelchair and started walking, thankfully with a limp. I turned and looked at him.

"One last job. We have to clear customs."

"Yeah."

"You fellows are on your own with them," chimed in Brigitta.

"No problem."

We waited in line until it was our turn.

"Passports, please."

I gave mine and Willard gave his to a couple of agents.

"These are in order, but you do not match your pictures. Please step over to that room."

He pointed to a bare room twenty feet away. We walked over and were ushered in by another agent. He brought out an old Polaroid camera and took our pictures. He then told us to sit down in some plastic chairs next to the wall. We waited. Brigitta came over.

"Don't worry. They do this all the time."

Ten minutes later they called us back to their counter. Everyone else had been processed. They laid our pictures on the counter and then placed different beard and mustache acetate overlays on them, comparing them to the passport pictures. They had some good matches as far as I was concerned.

"That's a good one, there, don't you think?"

They weren't amused. They picked a different one, taped it in place, and put it into an envelope. Then they stamped our passports and handed them over.

"That way."

"Thank you."

I walked, Willard limped, down some stairs to a door leading out onto the tarmac. The stewardess was there waiting for us.

"It was kind of you to wait. *Danke schön.*"

"*Es freut mich.* A friend of Brigitta's is a friend of mine."

We smiled, received our tickets back, and passed through the door. The 707 was sitting about fifty yards away, out in the open, with a jet stairway attached to the front port hatch. I looked around. A chain-link fence came up next to the corner of the building about thirty feet away. Peering through it were our PLO buddies. I could see that one of them was Abu Sultan. I nudged Willard. Sultan looked over at us, and then I called to him.

"Abu Sultan, do you guys want us?"

He just looked. The stewardess with us stood quietly. The stewardess on the top of the stairway was waving to us to come, and I could see the pilot making faces and angry gestures through his windshield.

"You almost ruined things for us, you know?"

"It was a bad situation that you put us in, don't you think?"

"Yes, I suppose so. But we finished our job in spite of you."

I guessed he meant that they had gotten Josef Abi Assi.

"What's this we heard about the bus?"

"That was revenge for their man. It was a very bad thing. They will pay."

"I think you all will pay, Abu Sultan."

"Perhaps. It is all part of our fate. We accept it."

"I know. Good luck. . . . Say, will you see George?"

"He hopes not."

"Crazy fuckers," I whispered to Willard.

"Go back to America and tell our story."

"We will. Thank you."

Bill and I and the stewardess trudged across the tarmac and up the stairs. We both looked back from the top and waved to our friends.

They waved back. They were smiling. I was more worried about them than I was about George.

We walked in. There was nowhere to sit, of course. I saw Brigitta waving in the back. We walked back there among all the dirty looks and hard stares. She had saved us a couple of fold-down, flight crew seats.

"I always wanted to sit in one of these. I like the way the harness looks."

"It feels good too. Nice and secure."

We all three looked at each other and laughed. I tried to see out a window as we pulled out onto the runway. I couldn't see the gang by the fence. I straightened my head and squared my shoulders. The power and roar surged, and we started to roll. We thundered down the runway and took off to the smoothest flight I ever had.

EPILOGUE

The flight was uneventful. We had a good time. They gave us free drinks and plenty of food, and we got to tell the story to Brigitta and the other counter agents; the stewardesses rotated in from their work to listen to it. Things were quite festive in the aft section. We stopped once in Thessaloniki for some rain and drabness. I fell asleep for a while between there and Munich and woke up just in time to land. It was the end of their flight, so we hung around a little with the airline bunch before we deplaned. I got Brigitta's phone number and actually saw her a few times.

We shuffled out with our passports and nothing else and took a bus to customs. Our processing was routine. Our biggest job was to get back to Stuttgart. We still had quite a bit of money, so we changed it into DM, found our way to the train station, and got on a good train to Stuttgart. Once we arrived, Willard called up Guy. He came and picked us up. We got pretty good at telling the story. I could tell it in English or German.

The next day we went to the bank, and thank God my money had arrived. I gave Willard enough for his flight back to America, then I took the rest and bought a car. It was a great old bomb, a Ford Taunus with four on the tree. Willard made arrangements to fly a couple of days after we returned to Stuttgart. Before he left, we found the papers for his car. He had left them at Frau Zeyer's. After Willard left, I organized them and mailed them to George at the White House. I doubted that he would ever see them. I tried to call there, but I couldn't get through.

I followed the situation in Beirut pretty closely. Most of the descriptions of the war began with the attack on the bus. Reports said that a busload of Palestinians was returning home from a rally to celebrate the one-year anniversary of a guerrilla attack on the Israeli town of Qiryat Shemona. It was ambushed by Phalangist party gunmen; twenty-six died and nineteen were wounded. The Phalangists denied this and said that the bus opened fire on some people as it was driving through a Phalangist neighborhood. In any event, things went downhill from there. More and more people died. I watched in disbelief and horror as things worsened every day. It was really bad to watch the Holiday Inn get trashed. I read that Ahmed Rahmeh was killed by Israeli agents in a car explosion. I wondered about George and Abu Sultan, and everybody else.

I learned later that Willard had gotten a call from George. He was at his home in Reno when George called him collect. It went something like this:

"Bob."

"No."

"Bill."

"George?"

"This is George. I am in Beirut still. I need some money."

"Wait a minute. How are you?"

"I am fine, but I need money. Can you send me one thousand dollars?"

"No, George. Bob will send you money, whatever we owe you."

"I do not know how to reach him."

"I'll give you the number in Germany."

"I will send you your car, and you send me the money."

"No, George. I don't want the car, and you can't send it to me. How can you possibly have it anyway? It would cost you the thousand to send it. Call Bob. He wants to send you the money. He sent you the papers at the White House."

"I could not go back there."

"Tell me where he can reach you and I'll call him for you."

"I cannot tell you now. I will call you back."

"Look, George, I can't help you unless you tell me how to reach you."

"I have to go. I will call you back."

"George!"

That was it. And that was the last time we heard from him. I had the money for him, and I wanted to send it to him, but I didn't know how to do it. I've felt bad about it ever since. I still don't know what happened with him. I hope he's okay.

The rest of my stay in Europe was fine. I did three months in a foreign study program in Mainz. I lived with the family of one of my professors. The mother didn't like me or understand me. I traveled all over the place and had a great time, but it wasn't quite the same as the first part. The sense of foreignness and excitement just wasn't there. And I missed George. I still do. Maybe he'll read this and get in touch. I hope so. I'd like to hear the rest of the story.

(From left) Bob, Abu Sultan, Anna's mother Isabella, George, Anna, and Bill in a Beirut restaurant.

AFTERWORD

George Tanjanian was born in Baghdad on November 5, 1941, to an Armenian Christian family. He was an outstanding bicyclist and competed for the Iraqi Olympic team in the Mexico City Olympics in 1968. He obtained political asylum at that time in Mexico, claiming he would face persecution as a Christian if he were to return to Iraq. He married a Mexican woman and became a naturalized Mexican citizen.

After the time of the story presented here, he gained entry to the United States and lived in Detroit (from where he had come at the time of the story). He was convicted of visa fraud in the late 1970s and served nine months in a federal prison. Shortly after his release, according to later federal court documents, he embarked on an international human smuggling ring, which he led.

George was arrested in Miami on February 13, 1998. A federal investigation was initiated in October 1996 when immigration authorities at the border in El Paso stopped a Jordanian who had falsely claimed to be a US citizen and a Syrian who presented false documents. The investigation took place over a year's time and spanned five countries and included the actions of an undercover INS agent who posed as an alien smuggler with connections in the INS. He lured George to Panama, from which he was expelled and placed on a flight to Miami, where he was arrested. He was transported to El Paso for trial.

According to court documents, George allied with Mexican immigration officer Salvador Moreno to facilitate the transportation of hundreds of Middle Easterners through Mexico into the United States. George owned travel agencies in Havana and Quito, Ecuador, through which he arranged travel. He charged $10,000 to $15,000 per person, charging more if the person was politically or legally "hot." He charged an additional $4,000 to $10,000 for transportation in the United States. The major destinations were Los Angeles, Las Vegas, Detroit, and New York.

According to court documents, George would recruit people from the Middle East who desired transport to the United States. He used smuggling stations in Jordan, Syria, and Greece, and staging areas in Thailand, Cuba, Ecuador, and Mexico. It was estimated by federal authorities that the smuggling ring had been in operation for over twenty years, had smuggled hundreds of people, and had netted George $1.25 million. Included in the indictment was the allegation that in the early 1990s, a boat owned by George carrying eight Pakistanis sank, resulting in the deaths of the crew and the eight passengers. This act resulted in the enhancement of his sentence.

The federal case against George Tanjanian was filed February 26, 1998, in US District Court for the Western District of Texas. Seven aliases were listed; in addition, he was known as "George the Iraqi." After agreeing to a plea agreement on October 17, 1998, he was convicted of conspiracy to defraud the United States to transport aliens and four counts of aiding and abetting, bringing in and harboring aliens. While he had transported known criminals, including a Yemeni who was wanted for genocide, and many of his clients came from countries that exported terrorism, he was not charged with any offenses associated with terrorism. He was sentenced to thirteen years in federal prison, at that time the longest sentence ever handed down for these offenses. George was committed to federal prison. He died there on November 30, 2001, shortly after his sixtieth birthday.

I learned these things about George many years after our time together in Beirut. I must admit that though the crimes are egregious, if not heinous, I still feel love for him. I have a hard time judging him. He came from a different world where the rules for survival were utterly hardened by war and brutality. He was a criminal, but to me George was a brilliant operator and a caring friend. RIP George.

ACKNOWLEDGEMENTS

No man is an island. Every human endeavor is a product of more than one person's efforts. Many thanks are due for this book.

My first thank you must go to Bill. Besides being a great friend and perfect traveling companion, Bill was, and is, fun, generous, funny, adventurous, forgiving of any transgression and unstoppable. To say that I couldn't have done it without him is an understatement: I certainly wouldn't have done it without him and, even if I had tried, it would have been a pale version of the actual event. Thank you my friend.

I wrote this between the years of 1985-95 while I was in medical training and in my first years of practice. I almost had it published by a major house, but the editor lost interest and it ended up sitting in a box and on my computer for decades. I will describe its reincarnation at the end of this section, but I owe my college classmate, friend and fellow author Robert "Skip" Cummins great thanks for telling me about his experience in publishing his book "Mastering Yourself", and particularly for telling me about Jared Kuritz of Strategies Public Relations. Thank you, Skip.

Jared is a literary consultant who engineered the publication of "Meet Me in Beirut." A true expert in the field, his resources and actions have allowed my story to be shared. It was Jared who informed me of George's history subsequent to our time together. Thank you for everything, Jared. It has been a great pleasure working with you.

Susan Tibolt is my wife and long-time love. She is also an avid reader of "popular fiction" and knows a good book when she sees it. I couldn't remember when she had or even if she had read "Meet Me in Beirut", so last year I asked her to read it. I was eager to hear what she had to say. When she had finished, she told me that the first hundred pages were garbage and must be discarded, and to condense that part into ten pages, get rid of the sophomoric antics of my life at that time, and get on with the real story. Otherwise, she said it was a real page-turner. I was very pleased because she is the most honest person I know and would never say anything she didn't believe. It was this act, coupled with a timely reunion with Skip, that led to the book's publication.

To all the people whom we met during our adventure I send my thanks and admiration. I really learned about hospitality and generosity in the Middle East. The people there are so passionate about loyalty and commitment. I was struck by the common thread of unfulfilled yet undying love throughout their lives, song, and art. This is the gift for which I am most thankful.

ABOUT THE AUTHOR

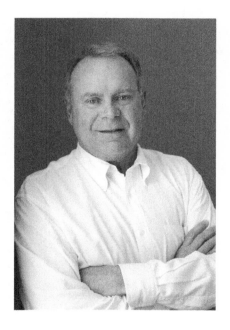

Bob Tibolt grew up in Massachusetts for the first eleven years of his life, then moved to Reno. He graduated from Reno High School. He returned to New England to attend Dartmouth College where he majored in English with a concentration in literature and creative writing. Subsequently, he attended graduate school and medical school in Texas, then moved to Oregon for internship and residency in ophthalmology. He practiced in Oregon for thirty years and retired in 2018. At that time, he and his wife Susan returned to Nevada where they now reside in Las Vegas. They have two sons, two grandchildren, and are happy to be back home in Nevada.

Bob is also a mapmaker, having learned the craft at Dartmouth from Geography professor Van English, who was renowned in his field and personal cartographer to General George Marshall, US Army Chief of Staff in World War II.

Bob has a studio and gallery in Las Vegas, ArtMapMaker, and made the map in this book.

Bob enjoys hiking in Red Rock Canyon and riding his bike, among the many other joys of living in Las Vegas.